My Secret Diary

MY SECRET DIARY

JANINE PHILLIPS

SHEPHEARD WALWYN

Typesetting by Alacrity Phototypesetters, Banwell Castle, Avon.
Printed and bound in Great Britain by Biddles Ltd,
Guildford and King's Lynn.

TO THE MEMORY OF
MY BROTHER WOJTEK

*This is going to be my
secret diary, and on no account to be
read without my permission.*

16th May 1939

TODAY is my nameday and my birthday. I am ten years old and too little for my age. "Niusia* has hardly grown since last year", Aunt Stefa said and it hurt. I try to eat a lot but I am still only one metre and two centimetres tall. (Two-and-a-half centimetres when I stretch myself.) Though my hair is quite long, I can almost sit on it.

I had lots of presents. Two books, a polka-dot ball and some sweets. From Mama and Papa a Shirley Temple doll, and a box of crayons from my brother Wojtek. My friend Ania gave me this diary which I am going to keep till the very last page. It could be for many years because it has one thousand pages. Ania is my best friend and I shall let her see some of my entries. I like her much better than my cousins. In fact, Tadek and Jurek are often disagreeable and not only to me. Today, for example, they went to the attic and wee-wee'ed into Auntie Stefa's preserving jars. She was furious with them. She managed to spank Tadek but Jurek ran off. It's always the same. He is the worst of the lot and hardly ever gets what he deserves. He couldn't even stop being beastly to me today. Though he knows it's my birthday because I've told him so.

After dinner I went with our maid Irka to the cellar to make a special ice-cream. We put ten yolks and some milk and sugar into the mixer, then we packed some ice and salt around it. I turned the handle and every few minutes we stuck our fingers into the mixture to see if the ice-cream was set. Yum yum, it was lovely. I like making ice-creams best of all. We banged on the saucepan to announce it was ready. And who should be in the queue first, Jurek of course. Though he hardly ever hears when Aunt Stefa calls him. Everybody enjoyed the ice-cream. Mama and Auntie Stefa had some with black cherries soaked in vodka and dear Papa left his portion of ice-cream for me and made do just with the

---

* Pet name of the author as a child.

1

vodka. I like Papa a lot because he often laughs and seldom gets cross.

17th May 1939

MRS Nowak came today to do the washing. Grandpa got niggly. He hates the washdays. The whole house has been topsy turvy from seven in the morning till eight at night. I felt sorry for the horse. Poor Samson has been pulling so many barrels of water from the well. Grandpa thinks it's a waste of good water and he said to Mrs Nowak that she uses too much of it. Mrs Nowak told Grandpa to make up his mind whether he wanted some clean sheets and shirts. If not, she wasn't going to waste her time. Grandpa reminded her that he was the boss in his own house, but Mrs Nowak had the last word. She pointed out that his job was to get the water and afterwards to pay the bill. Grandpa walked out in a huff and told Samson exactly what he thought of Mrs Nowak. I am glad it was out of her earshot for I quite like Mrs Nowak. She doesn't mind chatting with me while doing the washing. Her hands are red and puffed up because she does the washing for the big houses every day of the week except Sundays. I helped her sorting out the sheets, pillow cases and all the whites which were not so dirty. The linen went into a big boiler and the lot onto a hot kitchen range. Mrs Nowak put in some soft soap and some washing soda, then two buckets of water (and some extra to spite Grandpa) and covered it with a heavy wooden lid. The second batch of soiled clothes went into a wooden tub. She coaxed the dirt out by rubbing and squeezing the linen until the soap bubbles rose up to her elbows. Then I held a bucket underneath the tub, while Mrs Nowak pulled out the wooden stopper. I was amazed how dirty clean water could get. After rinsing, we hung the big items in the attic and the smaller bits and pieces on the barbed wire fence. In no time the washing was almost dry and ready for mangling. I helped Mrs Nowak to stretch and fold the sheets. In they went to a wicker basket. If any parts of the linen were too dry, Mrs Nowak took a mouthful of water and blew out a fine spray to remedy the situation. I tried to do likewise but it was not as easy as it looked. One needs years of practice, Mrs Nowak said, and I believed her. After tea we went to a mangling shop at the other end of the village. The mangling is done before, or even instead of, ironing. A heavy press loaded with stones is pushed over two wooden rollers upon which sheets and suchlike have been carefully wound. The press is moved to and fro by means of a handle. I quite enjoyed myself helping Mrs Nowak.

18th May 1939

JUREK, Tadek and Wojtek were discussing secrets and I was listening through the keyhole. Tadek said that Irka "was with child". I'll have to ask Ania what it means, but I have an idea it's something bad. I didn't hear any more because Jurek caught me listening. He was nasty to me and called me "little squirt". So I told him that I heard everything and furthermore, that I am going to tell Mama all about it. He grabbed my arm and started to twist it. I kicked him twice but my arm was very painful and I had to scream. Then Tadek said if I don't tell Mama, he'll teach me to ride his bike. I settled for that, but I am still going to tell Ania. Afterwards, I went into the kitchen and watched Irka peeling potatoes. She looked just the same but I noticed she'd been crying. I thought it best not to bother her.

We had pork schnitzels, cucumber salad and some new potatoes for dinner. For dessert, we had a cherry compôte which I like best of all. Fortunately I managed to give my plate of soup to our bitch Pempela. Although she's only a mongrel, she is highly intelligent. At meal times, she always sits under the table next to me. The trouble is that her table manners are not what they should be. She laps her food so noisily that everyone can hear her eating.

Mama gets cross if I don't finish my soup. Today, however, everybody was talking at once and Pempela was able to enjoy my soup in peace. She knows that I am her best friend. She certainly is my best friend too. I think her quite handsome, although people say her ears are too long and her legs too short. Well, so be it, I still think God would have a job to find a better soul among our lot.

May 21st 1939

TODAY is Sunday and we've all been to church. Grandpa drove us in his new carriage. For this special occasion Samson was beautifully groomed and he wore a new harness. The carriage has maroon leather seats and two brass lamps, one on each side. In the sun they shine like pure gold. Grandpa is very proud of his new carriage and said it was smarter than Radziwil's. I was wearing my pink dress, white coat and white bonnet with pink apple blossom around the brim. Though I would much rather have it trimmed with red cherries like Auntie Stefa's hat is. Wojtek, Tadek and Jurek had to behave themselves during the journey because Grandpa said so, but as soon as they set their feet in church the devil got into them. They started teasing the girl in front. Jurek tied her pigtails to the back of the chair she was sitting on. And when the priest intoned "Te Deum", she couldn't get up until Mama untied her ribbons. Wojtek got a loud smack across his hands though Jurek did it. I expect God must have heard it too because everybody turned their heads to look at Mama. I don't know why the boys come to church at all. They won't go to Heaven. Wojtek and Tadek might manage to go to Purgatory but Jurek's sure to end up in Hell . . . and they may not even have him there.

After the mass we stopped outside the church to exchange news and views and bits of gossip. Ania wasn't there but her two sisters Ela and Franka looked very grown-up. They wore high-heeled shoes and carried handbags. I wish I had a handbag with a mirror and a comb, and a purse, now that I've saved thirty-five groszy. Papa gave me twenty, ten groszy I saved from last Sunday's collection, and five groszy I earned from Wojtek for cleaning his shoes. He was going to give me ten but I suppose I was lucky to get anything at all.

22nd May 1939

I AM in bed with a sore throat. Mama has been putting a hot compress on my neck. I hate spirit compresses because afterwards my neck burns worse than my throat. Mama took my temperature and it was thirty-eight point five, which isn't very high because last year I had almost forty. Papa came from Warsaw for the weekend and he said that as soon as I get better he'll buy me a bike. I must get better very soon. I hugged my dear Papa ever so much. Irka brought me a cup of hot milk with some butter, garlic and honey. It smelt horrible and tasted even worse, but I drank the lot. Irka sat on the edge of my bed to make sure that I did. I asked her if she liked children and she said she did those who behaved themselves. I wish Ania would visit me. She's bound to know all about "being with child". Irka is very nice and everybody likes her. She has lots of freckles on her face and on her arms and is pretty big around. I feel sorry for her because she is an orphan. Her stepmother lives in the Jadwisin village with her half-sisters and brothers. Irka goes there on Sundays but she says she's always glad to come back to Grandpa's house. She told me that although Grandpa has a big mouth, he also has a big heart. And Grandma, being ill, hardly ever interferes. I go to Grandma's room only sometimes because she suffers from headaches. But when I go there I usually get a big glass of ginger beer. She keeps it on a window-sill, in a large jar. On the bottom of the jar, underneath the liquid, there is a big mushroom growing. It looks horrible but the beer is nice.

24th May 1939

I AM better now but must stay indoors, Mama says. Somebody has been nosy. Two days ago, I left my diary in the drawer of my table. This morning, however, it was on the table. No marks for guessing who the culprit was.

Mama said that I shall have to learn the Catechism because I'll have to be confirmed soon. I am dreading the day when I have to go to confession. I have so many sins that I doubt if I can remember them all. Some of my friends write their sins on a piece of paper. Olga lost her list before she even got to church and was frightfully worried. She was so petrified that she couldn't even utter a single word. Her Father Confessor thought that she had no sins and praised her to high Heaven for being so good. I hope I shall get absolution. Anyway, Jurek got his.

26th May, 1939

AUNTIE Stefa took Tadek, Wojtek, Jurek and me to Warsaw to collect our end of term school certificates. My marks were as follows: Four very good, two good and three satisfactory. I was quite pleased with my efforts but Mama was not. After all, four very good ones is not too bad. But Mama said they were for the wrong subjects. Sometimes I feel I can never do the right thing to please Mama. She wants me to do better in spelling and also in arithmetic. I hate sums and am always making mistakes, even when I try to concentrate. My friend Krysia is good at sums. During tests, she generally finishes her paper first and passes the answers around to those who are not so good at it. Jolly sporting of her and it seems to work quite well. Anyway, I've easily passed to class four which will start next September. We'll have a new teacher. Miss Kalinska is in charge of class four. She's a super teacher. Everyone likes her. Some pupils are really mad about her but she has no favourites. She's fair and she jokes a lot. Mr Jarosz likes her too. At breaks, they often walk together and I saw them dancing cheek to cheek at our Shrove Tuesday party. He might be her sweetheart, though he's quite old and not very good-looking. He smells of cigarettes and has yellow teeth not unlike our Samson. Only Samson's teeth go quite well with his horsey face. I think Miss Kalinska should marry our geography teacher. For one thing, he's very keen on exploring, and for another, his pockets are always full of peppermints. I shall never marry and for a good reason too. I don't like boys!!! Perhaps I ought to finish up being a nun. It's a possibility, except I don't know whether I could put up with such long hours of praying, and maybe I have too many sins. I'll have to count them one day.

28th May 1939

AT last Ania came to visit me. We had a jolly good natter about everything. Apparently, Ania's mother said to her that another baby was joining them. Ania was so put off by this sudden news that she forgot to ask her mother where the baby was coming from. So, I told her about Irka "being with child" and we came to the conclusion that both babies were coming from the same place. However, the question is from where? Ania is going to try to find out from her older sisters and she'll let me know.

29th May 1939

TODAY Papa arrived early from Warsaw and in the after-noon we went fishing. I caught a full jar of tadpoles, but Papa caught not a thing. Nonetheless, he was cheerful and we sang lots of songs together. On the way back Papa bought two kilos of fish and put it in his net and looked very happy. Though he was a bit grumpy with me when during supper I mentioned that the fish came from the fishmonger. I don't see why because the fish tasted just as good as if it were caught by his own hands. I wish I could hold my tongue. Sometimes I say things that I later regret. I hate upsetting Papa. Fortunately, he soon laughed and we played netball till it got quite dark. Grandpa's house has no electricity as yet and we use oil lamps and candle-light. I often write this diary by the candle-light, when I am in bed. But I don't mind that. I much prefer being here in Grandpa's house than in Warsaw. Here, there are lots of things to do and there is a large garden to play in. In Warsaw, we usually go to a park or walk about the streets. Though I like going to cafés. But, fortunately, most of our summer vacations, Christmas and Easter holidays are spent here, because it is Mama's home and she adores being at Borowa-Góra. Also, Grandpa is very old, and Grandma is poorly, so Mama likes to be here as often as she can. She also finds it trying to be apart from Auntie Stefa who is her twin sister. Mama and Auntie Stefa look alike. I sometimes have a job to distinguish their voices, and their feet are absolutely identical. They even have the same number of corns on their toes — five each. Mama is half-an-hour older than her twin sister, and Aunt Stefa never lets Mama forget it. They used to dress alike but now they only think alike. They both adore Papa quite a lot, only it doesn't show so much with Mama. I am not surprised they like Papa because he is terribly nice and always looks smart. He wears a black bowler hat. I noticed how well it suits him when we went fishing.

1st June 1939

HOORAY! My bicycle has arrived. I am so excited I can hardly hold my pen. It's a beautiful bike; red and black with a yellow stripe on the frame and mudguards. And a brown and yellow net on the back wheel. Papa lowered the seat for me as far as it will go and I can just about reach the pedals. He said that I'll have to hurry up and grow a bit to fit my new bike. So I ate all the food today, including the soup. Mama likes my bike too. She's been trying to learn to ride it. Wojtek was holding the bike while Mama pedalled and steered. Then he let go of the bike and Mama rode right over Pempela, quite unable to stop. Pempela squeaked, Mama cried and there was a crash. I thought that was the end of my bike. But somehow, neither Mama nor Pempela suffered any injury. And even the bike got off lightly — only one small dent and a broken bell. The trouble with Pempela is that as soon as anyone tries to chase her, she just lies on her back and waits for her tummy to be rubbed. And generally everyone obliges. Poor Pempela, she didn't know that Mama couldn't stop. Without a second glance at the bike, Mama gave up the idea of learning to ride and went to console Pempela. I could not help feeling that perhaps it was for the best. Whether Mama is too big for my bike, or my bike is too small for Mama, the fact remains that she is not a sportswoman. Mama is not very good at games. She can't even play croquet. She can't hit the ball, but somehow, the ball always hits Mama. The best sportsman in our family is my cousin Tadek. He's tall and he often wears long trousers. He can play most games. Wojtek is good at some games and very good at drawing. But Jurek says he is good at everything. Perhaps I should ask him to repair my bicycle bell.

2nd June 1939

THE month of June is a busy time and a fragrant time on Grandpa's smallholding. Every evening the roses are cut from the fields, sorted out into varieties and Uncle Tadeusz takes

9

them to his shops in Warsaw. Everybody has to help, including us children. My job is to transfer the flowers from the pickers' baskets into huge flat baskets and spray them with water. I love sniffing roses. My favourite colour is red and when I have my own house it will be full of red roses. Uncle Tadeusz does the supervising. He makes sure that everybody is pulling his weight, including Jurek.

This year, Grandpa has two students from the Horticultural College doing their practical course. They sleep in the old bakery and are never short of visitors. The girls from the village like them very much and our Irka likes them too. She brings them their breakfasts. The other meals they eat with us. Jurek and Tadek have been teasing Irka that Zygmunt (the ginger student) is her boyfriend. Tadek drew a heart in the sand pierced with an arrow and he initialled it I.Z. This could be true because I saw them canoodling in the barn. But I never told anyone about it, except Ania.

4th June 1939

I AM very excited because today we children are going to have tea on the Radziwil's estate. Mama has washed my hair and told me to sit in the sun while it is drying. So I might as well get on with my diary. The Radziwil's country house is in the next village of Jadwisin and it has ever so many rooms. A stranger could get lost in that house. There is a housekeeper and many maids. Also, there is a gardener, a footman and a host of other servants. The Radziwils are very noble and they own acres and acres of land. So, Mama told us to be well mannered, keep our left hands on the table during tea and never to talk unless we are asked questions. Irka has given us a double sandwich each so that we shouldn't eat too much while there. I am going to wear my primrose organza dress, clean white socks and my new sandals. Irka will be taking us and Zygmunt will be driving the carriage because Grandpa refused. Grandpa doesn't like the Radziwils because he said that they have more land than is good for them. He said that good land ought to be used and not left idle. Grandpa used to work on the Radziwil's estate in his young days but now is proud to have his own land and two houses in the village of Borowa-Góra. He always reminds us that all he's got has been earned by the sweat of his brow and help from God. But Papa says also money from Uncle Tadeusz. I must dash now, because Mama is calling.

9th June 1939

MAMA told us not to go into the fields because there is a mad dog prowling about. The dog has been seen by a farmer who had a lucky escape. He was so near that he actually saw the foaming saliva around the dog's mouth. The farmer took to his heels and ran for his life. Several volunteers got their guns and rifles and went to look for the mad dog. Mama says that rabies is a horrible disease and often fatal. When bitten by a mad dog one can die a dreadful death. She told me that rabies came to Poland from Russia. The Russian wolves and foxes spread the disease during the Great War. In cold winters, when fields and forests were almost buried by snow, huge packs of hungry wolves roamed at large, howling. It was a frightening sound. The animals used to eat the corpses of dead soldiers. Mama remembers it as if it were yesterday. Horrible, horrible. I get goosepimples at the mere thought. If there is another war we might get more wolves. Papa said that there was going to be a war with Germany. And at school, last term, we were taught how to use gas masks, should there be a war. Also, we've been encouraged to save our money in the P.K.O. by buying special stamps. In my book I have one zloty and twenty groszy worth of stamps. Our teacher said that the money will be used to buy some ammunition for the defence of our country. I don't think the Germans have a chance. One can buy lots of bullets for one zloty and if everybody saves, then we can give Hitler a proper thrashing.

12th June 1939

MR Sota shot the mad dog, so today we went to pick wild strawberries. They were growing almost anywhere and everywhere. I must have put twice as many into my tummy as in the basket. Mama kept on calling me because she was afraid I'd get lost. I don't mind woods, not even the huge ants. I've come across several ant-hills made of pine needles. They must have used hundreds and hundreds of needles to build such large mounds. I know it's dangerous to go near an ant-hill but something always lures me towards it. I could watch them for hours. We had a lovely picnic. Hard-boiled eggs, cheese sandwiches, and bread beer. It was so cool and beautiful in the wood that I wouldn't mind living there. I like the smell of resin and the whispering of the trees. I like the tiny flowers and the moss.

16 June 1939

GATHERING hay from the meadow is much more fun than picking flowers. One can make huge haystacks, climb right to the top and then slide down. I like that. We generally go with Grandpa. Today he harnessed Samson to a cart and drove us along a dusty road. It was already hot at ten in the morning and Samson was in one of his moods. We got as far as the figure of Blessed Mary at the crossroads. Grandpa stopped to put some flowers there and while he was offering his prayer, Samson got fed up waiting and turned back. We had to chase him for about a hundred metres. He just would not respond to Grandpa's calling. I'll say that much for Samson. He certainly knows his own mind. When he doesn't want to do something, he gets as stubborn as a donkey. Grandpa told Samson exactly what he thought of his impish tricks and gave him a smack across his bottom. All the way to the field Samson pretended to be too weak to pull the cart. In the end Grandpa had to get off and lead him on. However, as soon as Samson got a whiff of drying hay, he felt better. Grandpa had a job to keep up with him. I think our Samson is human inside and horsey outside. In no time we piled up the hay onto the cart and I had a job to climb up. Sitting on top, I nearly sank in it. I had to lie flat on my back. It was as if floating on a cloud, so high up and so soft. Lulled by the gentle rocking and the scent of hay, I fell asleep, dreaming of Heaven.

19th June 1939

I woke in the middle of the night hearing gunshots. Everybody got up to see what was happening. Apparently, Grandma, who stays in bed all day, decided to get up at night. She took an air gun and went to the orchard to frighten the thieves who, she was sure, were stealing the fruit. But it was Uncle Tadeusz who was patrolling the cherry orchard and making an awful lot of noise. In order to scare off any trespassers he fired his gun. Grandma, thinking that he was the thief, took a pot-shot at him. In the end Uncle Tadeusz had to throw down the gun and put up his hands as Grandma commanded. Had it not been for the fact that Grandma is a bad shot, Uncle Tadeusz wouldn't be here to tell his mother off for this unusual encounter. They had a jolly good row and everybody had a jolly good laugh. It went on well into the small hours of the morning and finally it had to be smoothed over by a drop of vodka. This was the first time I noticed that Grandma has no hair. She is absolutely bald and always wears a scarf which looks like an Indian turban. Grandma must have been in a great hurry to have forgotten her turban. I asked Mama what happened to Grandma's hair. Mama said she lost it through worry. Immediately, I started to worry about the fact that I worry quite a lot. I should hate to lose my pigtails which took many years to grow.

20th June 1939

AFTER last night's episode, Grandma lost her sense of humour and shouted at everybody including her beloved dog Gabriel. To us, this yapping dog always seems more like Lucifer. But not to Grandma, she calls him an angel. He has a nasty habit of hiding under Grandma's long frock and snarling at anyone who comes too near. Today, however, Grandma scolded the dog, then accused Irka of pinching the skin from her hot milk. She told Mama that she didn't know how to bring up her children. Mama retorted that it was a good thing that Grandma was such a poor shot or she'd truly have had something to grumble about. Grandma banged the door, lay on her bed and got a nasty headache. After that, everybody went quiet.

25th June 1939

WE had a lovely party on midsummer's night. In the garden, we had lanterns hanging from the trees. They were made from coloured crêpe in red, orange, yellow, mauve, blue and green. When it got dark, the candles were lit and it looked amazingly beautiful. Later on, Uncle Tadeusz lit the bonfire. The night was warm and so still that the flame rose straight up to the sky like a golden dagger. Everybody was very excited, including Pempela. She was waiting by my side for the goodies which she could smell. Papa and Uncle Tadeusz threaded two dozen sausages on a long wire and grilled them over the fire. Mama and Irka buried lots of potatoes in the hot ashes and Auntie Stefa handed tots of lemon vodka to the guests who were seated around the bonfire. I had some lemonade which Pempela doesn't like. I tried to give her some because some clumsy person stepped on her paw and she was in agony. I comforted her as well as I could and told her to sit under my stool. When the sausages were ready she felt better. I said that the baked potatoes were super and Papa said the same about the lemon vodka. Mama said that Papa likes his vodka better than her, but I think he likes them both the same. At midnight, we went to look for hidden treasure. Papa went with my music teacher Miss Wanda. When I wanted to join them, Papa said that I stood a better chance if I went in the opposite direction. I don't know how anyone can find treasure in the dark. So, I went into the house. There were only two sweets left in the tray. No doubt my cousins had the rest. I went to the kitchen thinking of giving one to Irka but I couldn't find her. The whole house was in darkness. Though I could hear some giggling and whispering. As soon as I asked who was there, it stopped. I felt scared. I thought of ghosts. My Great-Grandma died from shock in this very kitchen, Mama said. I asked her what sort of shock, but Mama said it was too shocking to talk about. When I am grown-up, I'll have a midsummer night party during the day.

27th June 1939

A DAY of disasters, that's what it's been today. First, Grandpa's teeth were chewed up by one of the dogs. He blamed Pempela but I am sure it was Grandma's little peke, Gabriel. He's not fussy what he eats. Just before breakfast, Grandpa put his teeth in a mug and Irka emptied all the dishes, including the mug, into the dogs' bowl. Grandma complained it was a careless thing to do as her little angel might have choked to death had he swallowed Grandpa's teeth. By then, Grandpa got pretty het up and said it would serve him right. Grandma replied that normal people kept their teeth in their mouths, and it beat her why Grandpa couldn't do the same. So Grandpa went to have it out with Irka. Irka, being sensible, as she always is, scrubbed the teeth with scouring powder and they looked just like new. Grandpa popped them in, smiled in the mirror, and all was forgiven.

The second misfortune happened after lunch when the key to the privy disappeared and the door was locked. The key to the privy usually hangs on the nail in the hall. When the key is missing people can tell that the privy is occupied. This system usually works quite well, until today. Someone lost the key, or got locked in and fainted, or goodness only knows what could have happened, said Mama, who returned from her third fruitless trip to the bottom of the garden. She wanted to know what was the point in locking up the privy. Was a pot of gold being kept in there? Grandpa told Mama to go in the bushes while he went to see what could be done. It took Grandpa the best part of an hour to get the door open. No-one was there, and nothing was missing, not even the key which, miraculously, was found to be hanging in its usual place. However, Jurek was missing, and Grandpa took his belt and went to look for him.

Finally, we had an explosion in the cellar. Practically all the bottles filled with home-made beer blew their tops. It sounded like a detonator going off. Pempela got so frightened that she hid under the sofa and stayed there for two hours. The cellar was in a dreadful mess. The beer, made from rye bread crusts, is very nice, but also it is very temperamental. It ferments quickly and is ready for drinking within a few days. Mama said it exploded because we've been having exceptionally hot weather. It was an awful waste of good beer, and everybody agreed that today was not our day.

29th June 1939

THE heatwave continues. It was thirty-one degrees in the shade yesterday. Today, we went for a swim in the River Narew. I had to bathe in my knickers because I haven't got a bathing costume. I wish I had a proper swimsuit with a top. I've been trying to learn to swim using the inner tube from an old tyre. But beastly Jurek kept on pulling off my knickers. Even so, I managed to dog-paddle for about two metres. The water was rather cold and the current strong so we didn't stay in for long. Auntie Stefa bought us an ice-cream each at the camping buffet. I had a "Penguin" covered in chocolate. It's my favourite. By the time we got back I felt very tired and my back was scorched by the sun. Mama made me lie on my tummy while she spread some sour cream all over my back and shoulders. The pain eased at once.

1st July 1939

IRKA has been making cherry dumplings which is the most delicious dish, as far as I am concerned. I helped her to stone the cherries. We used a hair-pin and it worked quite well. The cherry stones were useful too. We sucked them first and then we spat them out through the window. It was rather funny because Grandpa happened to be passing by and one hit him right on the head. He looked up not knowing where it came from. It was so funny that we couldn't stop laughing. Irka also likes cherry dumplings so we made lots and lots of them. She cut some circles from the dough and put five cherries in the centre of each one. I stuck the edges together very firmly, but even so, Irka had to go over mine again because I'm not very good at sealing pastry. We made fifty-seven dumplings altogether. When the water came to the boil, Irka popped in a few at a time and waited until they came to the top. Then, she fished them out and arranged them on our biggest platter. After that, she melted lots of butter and she fried some breadcrumbs in it until the crumbs became golden-brown.

17

She poured this over the dumplings. It looked delicious and tasted even better. Everybody enjoyed the cherry dumplings except Pempela. I gave her a piece of sausage instead because she looked so miserable.

4th July 1939

WE'VE been to the market in Serock today. Grandpa drove me and Mama in his new carriage. The road is rather cobbly and Grandpa was worried about the suspension. However we managed to get there before all the produce was sold out. Mama bought three kilos of butter, ten dozen eggs, seven kilos of smoked sausage and five ducklings. She also bought four cottage cheeses wrapped in horse-radish leaves which keeps them nice and fresh. At the Serock market one can buy almost anything. In his younger days, Grandpa used to sell his shrubs, trees and flowers there. That was before Uncle Tadeusz had his shops in Warsaw. Now, Grandpa only does the shopping there. Serock has many Jewish shops and one can buy bargains there. Mama and I went to buy some material while Grandpa gave Samson his elevenses. We always go to this shop because the Jewish lady is very nice and obliging. She gave me some sweets and told Mama that I am growing into a pretty lady. It pleased Mama and made me happy. Whether it was Mama's intention to begin with, or just reaction to the compliment, we bought many lengths of material. I chose some cream cretonne with little red flowers and some lovely silk with different wild berries and green leaves. I like that one best. Mama also bought some white and navy blue crêpe for her dress and several metres of cotton for sheets and pillow cases. Afterwards, Grandpa took us to Auntie Pola who is a dressmaker and lives on the outskirts of Serock. Aunt Pola gave us refreshing lemon tea with freshly baked poppy-seed cake. I don't like poppy-seed cake but I ate it just to be polite. Mama, on the other hand, enjoyed it and had two pieces. After tea we looked through a pile of patterns to choose the styles for our dresses. It was at this point that Grandpa became impatient. He started to drum his fingers on the table and kept on looking at the clock. He said that Samson was getting restless and that we must be going. I think it must have been Grandpa who was getting restless because Samson, with his nose in a bag, looked as if he had all the time in the world.

7th July 1939

PRESENTS apart, I like celebrating Mama's nameday even better than my own. Generally, she has a big party and lots of guests. They eat torts* and drink vodka. Mama bakes the torts and Papa gets the vodka ready. He made some with orange peel in it and some with lemon peel, and sampled them both. Mama said that if he carries on sampling the way he does, there won't be much left for the guests. Papa wanted to know, in Heaven's name, how was he to tell if the drinks were all right without tasting them. Mama had no answer to that. He definitely won the argument and to celebrate it, he poured himself another glass. When the guests came, Mama was wearing her blue satin frock. The gentlemen bowed, kissed Mama's hand and wished her many happy returns. Mama smiled and thanked them very nicely for the flowers and the presents they brought. Mama looked quite different today and quite pretty. The torts were very tasty, especially the chocolate ones. After the guests had drunk all the vodka, they were ever so jolly. Nobody took any notice of us children. Needless to say, the boys took full advantage of that. Like vacuum-cleaners, they got rid of any remaining food, then they turned the garden into a racing track. The noise was too much for Pempela and me. In search of peace and quiet we went to watch the grown-ups playing bridge. However, Uncle Tadeusz was far

* gateaux

from being peaceful. He was telling off Auntie Stefa for playing the wrong card. Auntie, having gone red in the face and moist around her eyes, inspired sympathy from the other two players. They sprang to her defence. Pempela looked up, put her tail between her legs and made her way towards the kitchen, and I followed her.

10th July 1939

A GREAT day today! Uncle Tadeusz bought a new Fiat. He drove it all the way from Warsaw in only half-an-hour. At the gate, he sounded the horn and pulled up outside the house with the back wheel stuck in the flower bed. Everybody came to see what was happening. Uncle Tadeusz switched off the engine, waved his hand and got out, beaming all over his face. Everyone was very impressed except Grandpa. He doesn't trust mechanical things and especially cars. Grandpa says that Samson is real value for money. He gives what he takes. At the end of each day there is enough manure to grow a sack of potatoes. Grandpa wanted to know what Uncle Tadeusz was hoping to get from his Fiat. After dinner we all went for a ride. Auntie Stefa and Mama sat at the back. I sat on Mama's lap, Irka next to us, and Wojtek and Jurek on fold-out seats. Tadek, being the oldest, had the privilege of sitting next to Uncle. Grandpa did not want to come. We begged Grandpa to give it a try, but he wouldn't. I think Grandpa gets more and more like Samson. He simply shrugged his shoulders and went off to the stable. Uncle Tadeusz got in, wriggled in his seat and said, "Right, here we go." He manipulated the gadgets in the front, but nothing happened. The car would not start. He tried the starting handle. No luck. "Everybody out", said Uncle Tadeusz. We scrambled out. Then Uncle got in and told us to push the car as fast as we could. After an awful lot of huffing and puffing, the engine started to splutter and finally got going. "All aboard", commanded Uncle Tadeusz. We piled in. "Ready?"

he asked. Mama and Auntie Stefa, somewhat out of breath, assured him that we were. "It was just teething trouble", explained Uncle Tadeusz shouting over the din. The car started with a jerk. Mama's knuckles were white from gripping the armrests. Uncle Tadeusz accelerated. "You see, she goes like a bird", he said. Only a thick cloud of dust was left behind as we bumpity-bumped along on our joy ride. We had a lovely spin but I think that Mama was glad to get her feet on the ground again. Mama thought that Uncle drove too fast and the cobbly road was too bumpy. I liked it, although I nearly had my dinner in my lap. The boys were fascinated by Uncle's motor car. They fiddled with every gadget and poked their fingers everywhere. When Uncle Tadeusz caught them unscrewing various nuts and bolts he got cross. He threatened to lock them up in the coal shed if they touched the car once more. The Fiat was put in the tool-shed and the tools were put out. From today, the tool-shed was upgraded to a garage.

12th July 1939

MY favourite breakfast is scrambled eggs with slices of fried smoked sausage. We don't get that sort of breakfast every day. It is only for special occasions and sometimes on Sundays when there are guests in the house. Usually, we have only rolls with butter and coffee. Irka gets the freshly baked rolls from the grocer's shop in the village. Sometimes I take the basket and walk to the shop. It takes me about twenty minutes both ways. Mr Podbielski, who sells the groceries is very obliging. He is a short man with bowed legs. I generally get two dozen rolls and some sweets for myself. Today I bought a bag of fudge toffees with a picture of a cow on the wrapper. I had two on the way back and gave two to Irka who said that I was a little darling. I liked that. Irka gets very tired in this hot weather and she puffs quite a bit. She poured some milk coffee into a jug, buttered four rolls and put slices of cottage cheese on top of each half. She put all this in a basket with two plates and two cups and took them to Zygmunt and Bolek at the bakery. I wanted to go with her but she asked me to be an angel and lay the table for breakfast. Grandpa's dining table is the biggest I've ever seen. It stands in the middle of the room and is covered with a white oil-cloth. There are twelve chairs around it. Sometimes, we have to get more chairs from other rooms when there are more people. But when we have guests, Irka always puts a tablecloth, and some paper serviettes in two glasses, one at each end. Grandpa sits at the top of the table and we must wait until he takes his seat. Grandma used to sit at the other end, but now she has most of her meals in her room. The grown-ups help themselves to their food first, and then we children. Grandpa always crosses himself before he starts to eat, but nobody else does. I expect it's because Grandpa is far nearer Heaven than any of the others. After the meal, we say "thank you" and then we are allowed to leave the table.

13th July 1939

IT'S been raining today at last. They've been forecasting rain for the past two days on the radio, but it did not come till today. By lunch time, dark clouds covered every bit of blue. Lightning danced across the heavens, flashing and lashing, grumbling and rumbling as if all hell was let loose. The rain came down drowning the dusty soil. I love the smell of rain. After tea, when the torrent became just a trickle, I took off my shoes and socks and went to paddle. Lovely, silky mud between one's toes is not everybody's cup of tea, but I enjoy it. Our geese like it too. Mama thinks it's silly. We never agree, Mama and I. What I like, Mama doesn't. I wish she were more like Papa, because Papa is old only outside.

After supper I had a bath in rain water. Mama and Irka heated lots of it on the kitchen range and filled the tin bath nearly to its brim. Mama scrubbed me with a loofah, but I insisted on scrubbing my feet. I can't stand anyone touching my feet. I seem to have more tickle there than anywhere else. After me, Mama had her bath and then the boys. Auntie Stefa inspected Jurek's neck and ears and told him to scrub them again. He said that he washed his neck, but Auntie just took one look and handed him the soap and the loofah. He argued it was a suntan, but Auntie said she'd never seen a grey suntan. I expect old Samson was grateful for a drop of rain. It saved him at least a couple of trips.

14th July 1939

WOJTEK is going to be a painter or a sculptor or even both, said Papa. He paints everything, landscapes, flowers and portraits. He did one of Pempela and it was a great success. She actually looks better than ever in the picture. Wojtek had a job to make her sit for him. I had to sit with her and tell her that not every dog has her portrait painted. That did not impress Pempela. So I had to feed her with goodies. The problem was that she gobbled them before Wojtek even had the chance to paint her yellow spots. The next piece of sausage, which was jolly difficult to pinch from the cellar, I cut into tiny bits and put one at a time into her mouth. All Pempela's troubles seem to disappear with every bit of food she swallows. I must admit Pempela's portrait was the best picture my brother has ever painted. Papa likes it too. He promised to buy a frame for it. Wojtek said that I could hang it in my room. It was nice of him. I, in return, have cleaned his shoes, the backs as well, all free of charge.

16th July 1939

MAMA and Auntie Stefa were busy today making preserves. Cherries were bottled and raspberries were made into jam. I had to pull off the stalks and pick out the maggots. The maggots seem to like raspberries much better than cherries. They nestle nicely inside raspberries and when one pulls out the stalks they waggle their heads. The raspberry jam Mama boiled in a large copper pan and then put it into glass jars for the winter. Mama also made a small jar of rose petal jam. She creamed some freshly picked petals from our mauve roses with an equal weight of sugar. I don't like that jam but it smells nice. She uses it when she bakes Danish pastries or croissants.

Mama and Auntie Stefa were telling Irka how times have changed since their childhood. How during the Russian revolution the Bolsheviks stormed the house looking for Tsarist sympathisers. How Grandpa hid underneath a pile of potatoes in the cellar. The Bolsheviks went through every sack of wheat, flour and every likely place that a man could hide. They thrust their lances into the potato pile and damaged Grandpa's eye. The sharp steel went right through the eye-ball. They took him away to prison and his eye saw light no more. Grandpa can still see quite well with his sound eye, but this shocking experience left him with a permanent scar, and not only to his face. Grandpa often sits in his chair telling the beads, and the empty socket of his eye fills with tears. I wish I could comfort my Grandpa but his worries are as many as his years and that's very many.

18th July 1939

IRKA'S been to the doctor and she's been crying. I was so sorry for her that I felt like crying too. I asked her what was the matter but she said it was nothing. I know there must be something wrong and I wish I could help. I offered her a sweet and then got on with the washing-up. I took a floor-cloth and wiped up all the water splashes. When Irka saw me doing it, she burst into tears. I put my arms around her and we both had a jolly good weep. I'm glad there was no-one around to interrupt us. When

Pempela came to inspect her bowl, she knew at once that things were not quite right. She came over to me and licked my knees. What a dear little dog she is. Irka and I worked in the kitchen, not saying much. Then Mama came in and she had nothing to say. After that, Aunt Stefa poked her head in, looked at Irka and me, and went out. I think we were glad to be left in peace.

19th July 1939

ZYGMUNT was sent home today. Grandpa told him to pack his bags and go. That's probably why Irka's been crying. If he is her sweetheart, then it does make sense. I should also cry if my sweetheart was sent away. Tadek's been saying that he has gone for good because he heard Grandpa telling Zygmunt off. I wonder what Zygmunt has done that Grandpa wouldn't do. Bolek is still here, but I don't think Irka likes him all that much. Zygmunt is much better looking in spite of his ginger hair. His eyes are blue and when he smiles, he has dimples, one on each cheek. I think Irka has good taste, because Zygmunt certainly is a handsome fellow. It's a pity that he had to go. I think Grandpa is too strict and he gets cross over almost nothing. It's Grandpa's age, Mama says. I agree with her. I can actually see Grandpa shrinking inside his skin. I wonder whether old people feel the same way as they look. I should hate to get old. In fact, I don't want to grow up. The grown-ups don't like doing many things which I like. And the things that I would never do from choice, they invariably enjoy. For instance, they drink many glasses of vodka and I couldn't even swallow a sip. The same with cigarettes, they smoke lots and lots of them and I don't like the smoke. Also, they get annoyed over things that don't bother me at all. That's why I prefer to be me at my age.

21st July 1939

FATHER Jakob came to visit us. He usually sees to our souls and Mama usually sees to his stomach. Father Jakob is rather plump and always busy. He wears a black cassock which is shiny on the seat. He has nice soft hands with fingers like chipolatas, a round head with black curly hair, and a pleasant face which turns pink in summer. Father Jakob is a saintly priest. He likes praying and he likes Mama's doughnuts, which he says are sheer heaven. This afternoon, having finished his tea, he started on our souls. First, he had a lengthy chat with Grandpa, then he went to talk to Irka. They were in the front room for the rest of the afternoon, and when he emerged, it was time for dinner. Mama and I laid the table, clean cloth, paper serviettes, the lot. Just as Mama was going to slice some cold meats, Irka reminded Mama that it was a Friday. "Good gracious", exclaimed Mama, dropping a piece of sausage. It just would not do to serve meat on a Friday in the presence of a priest, said Mama. She was so bothered about having nearly dropped a clanger, that she forgot about having dropped the sausage. Pempela, however, was not so particular about her religious ethics. She was already half-way through her "bit of good luck" when Mama remembered what she'd forgotten to pick up. "Get this blasted dog out of here", shouted Mama louder than usual. Mama would not calm down even though I pointed out that Pempela only had a nibble. Flushed and flustered, Mama ran to the cellar and rummaged through her store-cupboard. She fished out a jar of pickled herrings and arranged them on a serving dish. With bits of green lettuce and red tomatoes, a few slices of cucumber and radish, it looked very appetising. Irka and I said so. Mama took the dish to the dining room and I followed her. She apologised for keeping them waiting and passed the dish to Father Jakob. He looked at the pickled herrings, clasped his hands in front of Mama and, in a voice full of apology, he mumbled that fish did not like his tummy. And, if it were not too much trouble, a piece of ordinary sausage would do him fine. "Certainly", said

26

Mama running back to the kitchen. "There you are", said she, returning with a piece that looked familiar. I only hoped that God won't mind that Father Jakob finished up Pempela's sausage.

23rd July 1939

MAMA and Auntie Stefa are worried because Grandma is getting worse. She has an illness called diabetes, which Mama says is serious. Grandpa has been sitting by Grandma's bed and holding her hand. Irka is sad. The whole house is different. I wish Ania would visit me, or Pempela could talk. I know she thinks a lot, but that's not the same as talking. Although today is Sunday it seems like an ordinary day. We had no special breakfast, we even haven't been to church. Papa had to stay in Warsaw all weekend. The boys are away at their Scouts' camp. Normally it would have been nice without them, but today it's so sad that I even miss my cousins.

26th July 1939

JAN Kiepura, who is a famous singer, spent the day at Grandpa's house. He's a friend of Uncle Tadeusz, but today was the first time that I have actually seen him. He's neither old nor young, I would say in between. Mama said that he is good looking but Irka disagreed. One thing everybody agreed upon was that he can sing. After dinner, he sang *Sorrento* and in Italian, too. Mama and Auntie Stefa were absolutely enchanted. They mollycoddled him as if he were made of china. They kept on offering him sweets and chocolates but he refused them all. Apparently he eats garlic instead of sweets, because, he said, it was good for his voice. Actually, I knew he was fond of garlic as soon as he came in. Mr Kiepura sang many other songs and Mama was quite beside herself. She drowned him in compliments and he bowed his head, first to Mama, then to Auntie Stefa and back to Mama. I think he likes Mama better, because I saw him pinching her bottom. The musical interlude went on well into the evening. Everybody enjoyed it including Pempela and Grandpa. They both dropped off about half-way through *Palermo*.

30th July 1939

THE boys returned from their camping holiday. They've been to Mazury where the big lakes and forests are. Tadek said that they saw a bison, but only for a fraction of a second, because the bison was too scared. They brought a present for Papa which he sampled at once. It was a bottle of Zubrówka — vodka with a blade of grass in it, a special fragrant grass which the bisons eat. It gives the vodka a special aroma and a special flavour, Papa said.

After dinner we played a game of croquet and Uncle Tadeusz got into trouble for hitting Auntie Stefa's ball. She told him what she thought of his sportsmanship and threw the mallet at him, but it landed on the garden table amidst the coffee cups. Nobody thought it was funny except Papa. Auntie Stefa is as bad at games as Mama, only she doesn't think so.

1st August 1939

G RANDMA was taken to hospital in Warsaw this morning. Two men carried her on a stretcher to an ambulance. They drove off in a great hurry. Uncle Tadeusz went with them. Her poor little peke, Gabriel, ran after the ambulance, crying. Mama comforted him as well as she could, but she was pretty upset herself. Everyone had very little to say and Aunt Stefa and Mama busied themselves preserving gherkins. Bolek brought in a basket full of gherkins. We washed them and packed them into large glass jars. Into the spaces, Mama pushed whole stems and seed-heads of dill. Then she put a handful of black-currant leaves, a clove of garlic, and one bay leaf into each jar. She covered the gherkins with salted water, placed a wooden lid on top to keep them from popping up, and we took the jars to the cellar. Irka arranged them on a shelf and as we were going back we heard a cracking noise. One of the jars had cracked and Irka said it was a bad omen. I asked her what sort of omen. She said that Grandma had died. She said it with such conviction that I believed her. Later on, when we were alone in the kitchen, I asked her how did she know that Grandma had died. Did they not take her to hospital to make her better, I asked. Irka just nodded her head and said nothing. In late afternoon, the same ambulance pulled up outside the front door. The same two men brought Grandma back. Only now she was covered with a white sheet for it was only her body. Grandma died having never regained consciousness, just about the time Irka said she did. It was already too late for doctors. A hospital priest administered the last rites. Mama and Auntie Stefa wept, holding each other. Grandpa went to sit by Grandma's side. Uncle Tadeusz looked tired and drawn. Everybody talked quietly. Even the boys tiptoed around the house. I wanted to ask Mama why Grandma had to die but Mama seemed so miserable that I decided not to bother her. It is almost nine-thirty and the sun is already sinking to the ground. I wonder what's happened to Grandma's soul. Will Grandma's ghost sit beside her body tonight?

2nd August 1939

TODAY'S been like no other day. Mama and Auntie Stefa were busy rearranging the furniture in the house. They covered most of the windows and all the mirrors with black crêpe. The dining room has been made into a chapel and Grandma's coffin will be placed on a catafalque. Uncle Tadeusz brought in a kitchen table, covered it with a black cloth and put it in the centre of the room. Jurek and Tadek said that they saw Grandma's body. She had her mouth and eyes open, they said. Perhaps that's how the soul went out from her body, through her open mouth. When Mama went into the bedroom to wash and dress Grandma's body, I followed her. Mama took off the cover and I could hardly believe the waxy face belonged to our Grandma. Her mouth and eyes were shut now, but not quite. I had the feeling that her eyes were watching us, and yet, she looked completely dead. Mama bent over and kissed Grandma's feet. I felt sick. Why did she do that? This act of Mama's devotion filled me with disgust. Surely dead people are to be mourned but not to be kissed. I felt like saying so, but Aunt Stefa came in with some water. Mama cut Grandma's black petticoat and her best dress along the back. Then, she dressed Grandma, tucking in the cut ends under her body so they did not show. While she was doing it, she talked to her as if Grandma could hear. I'm sure Grandma couldn't ... though it would have given us a shock if she'd answered. Her arms were stiff as if made of wood. In the late afternoon the coffin arrived. It's a steel grey colour, almost silver, and it looks very smart.

3rd August 1939

FROM morning till dusk, our friends and neighbours were paying their last respects to Grandma. They brought in wreaths and flowers and placed them at the foot of the coffin. They knelt down, crossed themselves and said a prayer on

Grandma's behalf. The room was filled with white flowers and candles and smelt of wax and incense. The flames flickered and cast their pale light on Grandma's face. She looked so still and so serene and quite oblivious of what was going on around her. I wondered whether Grandma's spirit was looking down in satisfaction, or was it in another world, too far away from us all?

I went to the kitchen to help Irka with the tea and cakes. We had to borrow some extra glasses from our neighbour, so as to make twenty-five in all. Irka sliced four lemons and I put a slice in each glass. Then she poured a little very strong tea brew from a small pot, to be topped up later with boiling water. As the people came out from paying their respects to Grandma, they popped into the kitchen for a glass of refreshing tea. Mama says that sorrow makes people thirsty. Mama was right, because they were glad of a drop of tea and a slice of cheesecake.

4th August 1939

SINCE early morning everybody was getting ready for the funeral. The hearse arrived soon after eight. It was draped in black velvet embroidered with silver, and it looked very impressive. Two grey horses pulled the hearse. The driver was wearing a black coat and topper. Father Jakob came at eight-thirty. Mama made him a plate of scrambled eggs. They talked about Grandma and Grandpa and about the funeral procession. The bearers nailed down the lid on Grandma's coffin. I felt terrible. Then, they placed the coffin onto the hearse and arranged the wreaths and flowers around it. Father Jakob put on his white vestments and a black hat. One of the churchmen raised a cross high up into the air and walked out through the gate. The whole procession followed. First, the hearse, then Grandpa supported by Mama on one side and Aunt Stefa on the other. They both wore black frocks and their faces were covered by black veils. After them walked Uncle Tadeusz, Papa and us, the children. Next, all our relations. Father Jakob walked behind the family reading from the hymn book. Then followed the whole crowd of people who came to the funeral. The procession snaked its way along the lime avenue to the main road. We walked slowly towards the cemetery singing hymns. The sun was hot and the dust, disturbed by the horses' hooves, followed the hearse with the same devotion as the rest of us. After an hour and fifteen minutes we arrived at the cemetery. The horses turned through the tall iron gates without the slightest hint from the driver. No doubt they knew their way by heart. Grandma's grave was dug among the graves of our ancestors. The hole was deep with a pile of yellow sand beside it. The coffin was carried from the hearse on the shoulders of four men. Father Jakob conducted a short service. Everybody knelt down. They lowered the coffin. Mama and Aunt Stefa whimpered, Grandpa wept and I wept too. The gravediggers threw a shovel-full of soil onto Grandma's coffin. Somehow, it seemed wrong to me that Grandma should be buried beneath the same earth that the rest of us were free to walk upon. The grave was filled. A wooden cross was stuck at the head of the mound. Uncle Tadeusz and Papa placed the wilting flowers on it and the funeral was at an end. We made our way back in the mid-day sun, feeling utterly exhausted.

5th August 1939

GABRIEL has been missing since yesterday. We looked for him everywhere. Jurek and Wojtek went to search the fields. Tadek explored the garden and the outbuildings. I looked in every room in the house and even asked Pempela to help, but with no success. Gabriel had just disappeared. Only Grandpa had an idea where the little peke might have got to. He harnessed Samson to the carriage and drove to the cemetery. Sure enough, he found little Gabriel by Grandma's grave. He was covered in yellow sand and had dug a hole almost the size of his own body.

32

We were very moved by this example of Gabriel's love and devotion. Wrapped up in our own sorrow, we forgot about his loss. As from today, Grandpa took charge of him. Mama says that they need each other.

6th August 1939

IRKA has gone for a break to stay with her stepmother. I miss her very much. The whole house is still in mourning. Papa keeps on bringing bad news from Warsaw. He says that there's going to be a war, and he's usually right. Uncle Tadeusz has been listening to news bulletins on the wireless with extra attention. People talk about Hitler almost every day. Grandpa seems to be terribly depressed. Every day he takes Samson to the fields and stays there for hours on end. I'm truly fed up here. I wouldn't mind going back to Warsaw. There, at least, I should have my friends to talk to. From sheer boredom I've started reading *Quo Vadis*, and what a pleasant surprise. It's very interesting. I borrowed it from Irka. She reads quite a lot. When she comes back, we'll be able to discuss the story.

8th August 1939

I DIDN'T know that Tadek's father was too fond of his drink. I knew that Aunt Stefa's husband had gone away when Tadek was a little boy, and Jurek only a baby. Today, Aunt Stefa said to Tadek that he's getting more and more like his father. I asked Tadek whether he could remember his father. Apparently he can, but he doesn't like him. Tadek believes he once saw his father on a train. They sat opposite each other. Tadek became aware of eyes staring at him. He felt very embarrassed, and at once he realised it was his father. Instead of saying anything, Tadek ran off to another compartment. If I had been in his predicament, I should want to find out whether the man was indeed my father. I jolly well should have asked him why he had gone away. But Tadek doesn't like his father. In fact, he hates him, he said so. I hope our Papa will never go away. I couldn't live without my Papa. Aunt Stefa can live quite happily without her husband. She said she'll never marry again because men are only nice from a distance. Mr Leon lives in Kraków and it's over a hundred kilometres from Borowa-Góra. Maybe that's why Aunt Stefa likes him all right. I think he probably is quite well off because he has two gold teeth in the front and possibly some more at the back. He brings Auntie boxes of chocolates and calls her "little heart". She likes that and she certainly enjoys the chocolates. He called in today to offer Aunt Stefa his condolences. They had tea alone in the garden under the cedar tree. Mama said we were not to disturb them because they had little time and a lot to talk about. As one would expect, Jurek found an excuse to bother his mother every ten minutes. First, he said that he'd lost his penknife under the table and spent a quarter-of-an-hour looking for it. Then, he complained of feeling sick. In the end, Auntie told him to buzz off, but he still hung around until Mr Leon gave him ten groszy. When I told Jurek that he is a disagreeable creature, he called me "dirty knickers". I am certainly not "dirty knickers" because Mama makes sure that I change them every day.

10th August 1939

HEAT, and more heat every day from the blazing sun. The grass is brown, the flowers are drooping, there's not much water in the well. The temperature this afternoon was thirty-eight degrees. It was too hot for anything, so we followed Pempela's example and had a nap. After tea, when the sun had gone down, we went to help our Grandpa's brother harvesting the wheat. Great-Uncle Emil lives next door and he has a small farm and a large family. He also has a nasty hunched back and he doesn't like meeting people. He hardly ever comes over to Grandpa's house, but during the harvest time we sometimes offer to give him a hand and he's always glad of it. The wheat in his field has already been cut and we helped to tie it up into sheaves and then arrange them in stacks. I had to be careful how I walked in the field. The short stalks are as sharp as nails. The only safe way to walk in sandals is to slide one's feet as if skiing. Sandals are no use in fields, said Great-Uncle Emil. He always wears boots in winter and in summer. His legs seem to be all boots and his whole body all legs. Excluding his hump, there is very little trunk to Great-Uncle Emil. But even so, he has managed thirteen children, twenty grandchildren and two great-grandchildren. He grumbles that there are too many to remember their names, and he often refers to them by numbers. I should hate to be called number thirteen. Grandpa said the trouble with his brother Emil was that he had spent too much time in the barn and not enough in the fields. Although Grandpa and Great-Uncle Emil are brothers, they are not the greatest of friends. They only help each other in crises and shout at each other when things are all right.

11th August 1939

ON Fridays, Uncle Tadeusz generally arrives in his Fiat from Warsaw in time for dinner. Today, however, he came on foot and an hour late. His Fiat had broken down just outside Zegrze. Uncle Tadeusz had to walk three kilometres, swearing all the way, he said. When he got in he was so exhausted that he couldn't even swear. That is, not until Grandpa pointed out it was silly to expect too much from a mere motor-car. Uncle Tadeusz revived at once and said something really naughty. I can't say what he said because I don't know how to spell it. But I know it was naughty because Grandpa told him to mind his tongue in front of the children. Anyway, after they had finished quarrelling, Uncle Tadeusz borrowed Samson and went to fetch the car. It looked quite funny to see Uncle driving his Fiat which was being pulled by Samson. Grandpa also had a giggle and it was the first one since the funeral.

12th August 1939

THIS afternoon Mama has been teaching me how to crochet. It's been great fun sitting with Mama under the cedar tree, on a blanket. We played many gramophone records including my favourite tango *Jealousy*. Mama's favourites were anything sung by Jan Kiepura. Some of them Mama played over and over again until the needle was worn out. The boys have been putting all the used needles together in the box with the new ones. It took me ages to select a good sharp needle. Mama wanted it for her special Charleston. She kicked off her shoes and started to dance on the grass. Her feet jiggled and jerked as Mama skipped and swayed in rhythm to the cheeky Charleston. I've never seen Mama dancing so well. But just then, she remembered she was in mourning for Grandma, so we settled quietly to our handicrafts. Mama was stitching some dainty lace to a tiny white garment. I asked Mama who it was for. She said, "Well", and cleared her throat. I guessed at once she was going to tell me something secret which I already knew. "It's for Irka's new baby", she said. "The one she's been with child for?", I asked and noticed that Mama's eyes had nearly popped out of their sockets. She wanted to know whether Irka had told me all about the baby. And when I explained that it was the boys, she became even more surprised. So I thought it best not to ask Mama whether Irka was getting her baby from a stork or from under the gooseberry bush. Mama said that Irka will be coming back with her new baby probably next week or the week after. And, that is why she's been sewing such a little dress. It's for the tiny baby. I was so pleased that I hugged and kissed Mama on both cheeks. We both laughed in great relief. Mama, because she didn't have to explain things to me and I because she was quite looking forward to Irka's baby. I asked Mama if I could make something for the baby too, perhaps booties. Mama suggested a bonnet because booties were rather difficult to crochet. She said she'll find some wool and help me to make it. I was so thrilled that I did a little dance hoping our Grandma would forgive me for being too cheerful.

13th August 1939

THE thirteenth of August passed without a hitch. I am even beginning to think that it could be a lucky number for me. First, I heard some good news that Auntie Helena was coming back to Poland. She is Mama's youngest sister and she's been abroad for many years but I can remember her and Uncle Julek quite well. They have three children. Little Tania is six, Janek eight and Wicio nine. It'll be very nice to have Tania to talk to although she's only a baby in comparison with my age. The next good thing is that Mama has promised to get me a dress with a belt. It's terribly fashionable to wear a belt and I've never had one so far. A belt with a gold buckle would be rather fetching. As I went towards Mama's room to tell her about the buckle, I heard her saying to Papa that children nowadays were more astute than in her young days. She said that Irka's baby was common knowledge among the boys. It just beat her how they found out about it. Papa replied that the children will have to know sooner or later and it may as well be sooner. Then Mama said that she wouldn't be surprised if the children knew how the babies were made. I waited by the door hoping to find out, but Papa changed the subject. Somehow, I felt that approaching Mama about my belt and gold buckle just now was not a good idea.

15th August 1939

GRANDPA and Great-Uncle Emil had another row across the fence. This time it was about Great-Uncle Emil's pigs. The pigs came through a hole in the fence into Grandpa's garden for a siesta among the dahlias. Mother sow and her nine piglets made themselves nice and comfortable in a shady spot, but before they could doze off, Grandpa got them out with a broom. Mama sow did not think much of Grandpa's hospitality and she said so, loud and clear. That brought out Great-Uncle Emil who joined in with the pigs. Then, they exchanged the opposite-from-compliments. After that, they argued about the hole in the fence, which brought out the families on each side of it. Great-Uncle Emil's side had more support, and for every one word from our side they had three from theirs until Pempela joined in. Finally, where words had failed, bad apples took over. Our boys started hurling them at Great-Uncle Emil's grandchildren, until Mama told us to go indoors and allow Grandpa to carry on his quarrel with his brother in peace. So I went to my bedroom and opened the window but it wasn't quite the same. Although I could hear every word I felt excluded from the family forum. I don't mind Grandpa and Great-Uncle Emil having a ding-dong but I dislike it when Mama and Papa are having words. Because it usually ends up with Mama in tears and Papa in a bad temper. Fortunately, Papa doesn't stay cross for long. He prefers to laugh.

17th August 1939

JUREK told me that babies came from their mothers' stomachs. They grow inside it until they are big enough to come out. That's why Irka was so big before she went away, Jurek said. I don't know whether to believe him. Could Irka have eaten her own baby? No, that's too ridiculous altogether. Anyway, I'll soon be able to tell when Irka comes back. If it's true what Jurek says then her tummy should be much smaller. If it isn't, then Jurek is having me on, and that wouldn't be the first time. Jurek loves teasing people and playing pranks. At school, he is often impossible. His mark for good conduct is usually bad. Auntie Stefa thinks that he'll grow out of it, but I don't think so. It's a pity that she didn't choose to have a girl because they are quite nice when they are little and very nice when they are bigger. I hope Irka's baby will be a girl. We have too many boys as it is.

18th August 1939

WE had a useful drop of rain last night and everybody felt better for it. The plants in the garden perked up and so did the weeds. Uncle Tadeusz can't stand the weeds and he always grumbles that we, the children, don't do enough weeding. I hate weeding, but he wants the garden to look nice for his fiancée, Miss Aniela. She will be joining us for the weekend. Miss Aniela is sure to be clever because she is a teacher. Mama hopes that she is also very patient because Uncle Tadeusz's first wife was too good-looking and too lazy. Whereas Uncle Tadeusz approved of the former feature he could not stand the latter one. Uncle works very hard himself, and it niggles him when others are idle. Mama says that he's only happy when he's doing something. I can be quite happy when I am doing nothing, and Papa is like me. Papa and Uncle Tadeusz agree on many subjects but not about work. Uncle Tadeusz argued with Papa the other day that one lives in order to work, and Papa insisted that the other way round made more sense to him. I don't know who is right, but I do know that our guests prefer to be with Papa rather than with Uncle Tadeusz. I think it was my music teacher, Miss Wanda, who said that Uncle Tadeusz makes money whereas Papa makes people laugh, and it was simply a question of personal preference. I think Miss Aniela should suit Uncle Tadeusz because she is Uncle Julek's sister, and Uncle Julek and Auntie Helena have been married for many years

39

and they still like each other. So, in my opinion they should marry. The gipsy who comes to tell fortunes thinks that Miss Aniela is a good match for Uncle Tadeusz. She just took one look at their photographs, had her hand crossed with a silver zloty, and said they were made for each other. That gipsy is pretty good at fortune telling. She comes to the village twice every summer and has been doing so for as many years as I can remember. Aunt Stefa said she'd predicted many events, all Great-Uncle Emil's children and his grandchildren. She told her about a death in the family and now about the wedding bells on the horizon. At first, Aunt Stefa got worried that the bells were ringing for her. Without a moment's delay she gave Mr Leon the cold shoulder. But now she realises it wasn't a threat to her at all. The impending marriage was for Uncle Tadeusz. Mama said it would be good to have him settled but not so good to have another female about the house. Mama and I differ on the subjects of males and females. She actually prefers men and I don't see why.

20th August 1939

ON Saturday morning we were rushing and dashing about the house and adding finishing touches for Miss Aniela's arrival. Uncle Tadeusz put on his new suit and a pair of clean socks. There were fresh flowers in vases and a bunch of red roses in her bedroom. The privy seat was scrubbed and the floor sprinkled with sweet-smelling sawdust. Mama told me to cut some delicate tissue paper into squares in place of the usual wad of newspaper and keep the boys out of there until Miss Aniela "has been". Everything was set to welcome her in. On the last stroke of twelve Miss Aniela's carriage pulled up outside the house and Uncle Tadeusz, having mopped his brow, went to greet her. She wafted down in her sheer chiffon like a blue butterfly. I was amazed. She doesn't look like a teacher at all. She is quite young, has short black hair, cinnamon eyes and cherry lips. She wears white powder on her nose, pink rouge on her cheeks, black mascara on her lashes and Soir de Paris behind her ears. Uncle Tadeusz said she smelt delicious. Pempela took the opposite view. She sniffed Miss Aniela and then went to roll herself in a cow-pat. Then, she settled under the garden table next to me. People twitched their noses but owing to their good manners nobody asked where the pong was coming from. One by one, people excused themselves until there was only me and Pempela left. I took her by the collar and plunged her into a tub of water. Pempela was reluctant to part with her newly acquired perfume but I told her that the scent of cow-pats was not everyone's idea of bliss. Soon after Uncle Tadeusz had taken Miss Aniela into the greenhouse to show her his huge cucumber, Mama and Aunt Stefa started to talk about her. They were so busy that they never even mentioned about the pong. They talked about her hands and her polished finger-nails. Then about her high intelligence and low cleavage. Mama wondered whether a young woman who almost wore her bosom on her sleeve was an appropriate candidate to be Uncle Tadeusz's wife. I am sure Uncle Tadeusz doesn't mind it at all. Each time he took a sniff of Miss Aniela's Soir de Paris, he also had a peep down the front of her dress. I really don't see why Mama and Auntie Stefa are worried. Miss Aniela certainly was not worried about the weeds in the garden and I think that's a good thing. In fact she's quite jolly. She laughed a lot at Uncle Tadeusz's jokes and she smiled frequently at Papa. I wouldn't be surprised if Papa thought of her as a suitable sister-in-law.

22nd August 1939

JUREK has shot me! He was cleaning his air pistol up in the attic and I was watching him with my head bent forward. He forgot it was loaded. He pulled the trigger and the bullet scraped my cheek. The noise was terrific and really frightening. I thought that I was dead until I felt the pain. The blood poured down on my dress and by then I was screaming as loud as I could. Mama came rushing up to comfort me and assure me that I was still alive. Having fixed a plaster over my wound, she turned to look for Jurek. But he was nowhere to be found. After dinner, Jurek was sent to stand in the corner. Grandpa confiscated his air pistol and everyone was awfully nice to me. I went next door to show Great-Uncle Emil my injury and tell him all about it. He felt very sorry for me and said that I have been pretty lucky. Had Great-Uncle Emil seen the buckets of blood that came from my wound, I'm sure he would have felt that I was very unlucky indeed.

23rd August 1939

PAPA says that war is inevitable. I asked Papa why Hitler wants to attack us and Papa said because he's a greedy bully. I only hope he knows that peaceful people don't think him very nice. Grandpa went to see Father Jakob and asked him to say a mass to save us from war. Grandpa remembers many wars and he says that a war not only kills people but it also kills people's souls. That's why Grandpa feels that God ought to intervene, because there won't be many souls left in His Heaven. I quite agree with Grandpa.

24th August 1939

IRKA is back with the most adorable little baby girl I have ever seen. She's so small, even smaller than my biggest doll, Lila. She has a few hairs on top of her head, navy blue eyes and she hardly ever cries. And when she does the noise doesn't come out immediately. First, she waves her arms about, then she crumples her face and only after that the sound comes out. Her hands are very tiny and her toes no bigger than peppercorns. Irka is going to call her Danúska after the heroine from Henryk Sienkiewicz's novel. I think that's a lovely name and it will suit her quite well. Everybody has been coming to have a look at Danúska and Mama said that she is a pretty girl. Irka was absolutely glowing with pride, although she was shy at first. I must say that Irka's tummy has gone so it does seem that Jurek could have been right. The bonnet I crocheted is too big but Irka said it didn't matter because Danúska will soon grow to fit the bonnet. Irka was very pleased. She hugged me and said that she couldn't have crocheted anything like it herself. Mama gave Irka the christening robe she's made, and Auntie Stefa a shawl knitted from white wool. Irka thought the presents were lovely and she had many more things from the neighbours. The only person who was not enthusiastic about Irka's baby was Grandpa. He just took some sandwiches, mounted Samson and rode off to the fields. Mama said that little babies niggled Grandpa.

25th August 1939

I HAVE been helping Irka to bath Danúska. She's so small that our big enamelled bowl is quite adequate for the job. Irka poured in some warm water, measured the temperature by sticking her elbow in it, and lowered Danúska ever so slowly into what must have seemed to her like a huge swimming pool. She didn't cry one little bit. In fact, she enjoyed it. In a few minutes she was kicking her legs the way frogs do. Irka supported her head with one hand and washed her with the other. I soaped Danúska's feet and it was lovely. In no time half of the family gathered to watch our little bundle-of-joy's toilet. After the bath, Irka put Danúska onto a soft towel and gently padded the water off her spongy body. I have an idea she smiled at me, but Irka said it was the wind. I think Pempela is a teeny-weeny bit jealous. She raised her amber eyes at me as if asking, "Aren't I your favourite pet any more ?" I assured Pempela that she was and always will be, but we must take good care of Danúska for she's so little and is quite new to the world. Pempela appeared to be satisfied with my explanation. She wagged her tail and poked her wet nose at my knees. I am sure Pempela has a kindly heart underneath her furry coat. She used to play with the kitten from next door. She was as gentle with him as if it were her own little puppy. And, I am sure, she's going to like Danúska when she gets used to her.

26th August 1939

UNCLE Tadeusz and Miss Aniela are getting married by special licence on Sunday morning because they are in a hurry. She must have been favourably impressed last weekend. Mama and Aunt Stefa were somewhat put out when they discovered that their very own brother's plans and actions were far more advanced than they realised. Mama said that she felt like a proper ninny, trying to decide whether Miss Aniela was a suitable match for him, when the banns had already been called. The wedding will take place in Warsaw and it won't be a proper do because of the political situation. Though there will be a reception but only Mama, Papa and Auntie Stefa will be going. I have not been invited. I think that is a shame and I said so to Irka. Irka suggested that we could have a lovely picnic when everybody is out of the way. That cheered me up quite a lot, but I still would like to have gone to their wedding. Miss Aniela won't be wearing a pure white wedding dress. It's going to be off-white, and appropriately so, Mama said. Neither Mama nor Auntie Stefa are having new clothes for the occasion. They are going to wear their funeral hats but without the black veils. Mama has trimmed one hat with daisies and the other with forget-me-nots. She pressed her light grey costume, polished her high-heeled shoes and soaked her feet in charcoal water to soften the corns. Mama and Aunt

Stefa generally do each other's pedicure because they have identical feet and suffer from the same problems. They are going to
Warsaw by train from Zegrze and Grandpa is driving them to the
station. I might come to keep Grandpa company, on the other
hand, I may not.

28th August 1939

PAPA said that Grandma's funeral was less sombre than
Uncle Tadeusz's wedding. There was no dancing, and no
vodka. Champagne is not Papa's cup of tea. Mama and Aunt Stefa
were not overjoyed either. When they recovered from their
disappointment over Miss Aniela's mother, Auntie Stefa developed tummy-ache and Mama's old corns objected to her new
shoes. According to Papa, the only person who had a good time
was the best man. But Papa, being an optimist, thinks that a dismal
wedding day may well lead to many happy days to follow. Papa
said that many husbands look back on their weddings as the only
enjoyable day they ever had. Mama wanted to know whether he
was one of them and before he had a chance to explain, Mama's
neck got red. I am glad now that I didn't go to Uncle Tadeusz's
wedding because Irka and Danúska and I had a super time. Irka
made some delicious doughnuts with jam inside and icing sugar
on the outside. After we'd eaten them we could hardly move, so
we lay on the blanket and sang lots of songs. I asked Irka if she was
going to marry Zygmunt. She became embarrassed and said that
she was not. I wanted to ask her who then was going to be
Danúska's Papa, but I thought it best to change the subject. So I
asked her where Danuska got her soul from. Irka said it was from
Heaven, but it wasn't Grandma's soul. Grandma's soul would
have been too big and too old for Danúska. When I asked Irka
where God keeps all those souls, she smiled and said probably
under His feet.

45

29th August 1939

NEXT weekend we are going back to Warsaw. The trees look tired after the long hot summer and gossamer is floating in the air. The autumn has crept in and our holiday is almost over. On Monday, the fourth September, the school term will begin. Mama has been busy getting our uniforms ready. Wojtek is going to a new high school. He has a new smart jacket with a blue badge on the left sleeve. I have a new black overall with a white collar, two pockets and a belt. Papa bought me a new satchel and a pencil-box. At school, I shall be getting a whole set of new books. I am quite looking forward to starting in a new class. But I shall be sorry to leave Pempela, Irka and Danúska behind. Mama said that we shall be back for Christmas and then we can have lots of fun skating and sledging.

This afternoon we've been picking pears and apples so we can take some with us to Warsaw. Mama loves pickled pears and I like them too so we have been preserving some. It is very easy to pickle pears, even I can do it. First, we peeled, halved and cored some ripe pears. Then, we packed them into glass jars and poured some boiling spiced and sugared vinegar over them. And that is all, except tomorrow the liquid is to be reheated and poured over the pears again. You do that four times and after that the pears will keep for many, many months. Pickled pears are delicious with cold pork or lamb or gammon, but I like them best with cheese. I started packing my books and toys, but my bike will have to stay here, Papa said. I've tried to convince Papa that I could ride my bike in Warsaw's parks, but Papa said no. Papa can sometimes be as stubborn as Samson, the difference being that one can bribe Samson with sugar lumps.

31st August 1939

TODAY we visited the cemetery. Mama and Aunt Stefa knelt down at the foot of Grandma's grave and I did the same. There were some fresh crimson gladioli fanning out from the centre and two bunches of dahlias, white and yellow. There were three new graves nearby, one quite small. I asked Mama who was buried in the little grave. She inspected the bouquets and wreaths with pink ribbons and said it must have been a little girl. I was quite shocked. Somehow, I always thought of death claiming only old people. I should hate to be dead when there is so much to live for. Every new day is as exciting as a birthday present. In fact, the more I live the more I like it. On the way back, we called on Father Jakob to say goodbye and to arrange a convenient date for Danúska's christening. Mama is going to be her godmother and Great-Uncle Emil's son, Anton, the godfather. Papa is not very conscientious about church-going, and Irka feels that he wouldn't make a good godfather for Danúska. I think Papa would, because God likes Papa for not bothering Him too much.

1st September 1939

HITLER has invaded Poland. We heard the bad news on the wireless a few minutes after spotting two aeroplanes circling around each other. Just before breakfast, about ten minutes to ten, I was returning from the privy when I heard aeroplanes in the sky. I thought it was manoeuvres. Then I heard some machine-guns and everybody came out from the house to see what was happening. Grandpa said, "My God! It's war!" and rushed indoors to switch on the wireless. The grave news came in a special announcement that German forces have crossed the Polish border and our soldiers are defending our country. Everybody was stunned. With ears glued to the loudspeaker we were trying to catch the fading words. The battery or the accumulator, or both, were packing up. When we could no longer even hear a whisper from the wireless set, Grandpa turned the switch off and looked at our anguished faces. He knelt in front of the picture of Jesus Christ and started to pray aloud. We repeated after Grandpa, "Our Father who art in Heaven, hallowed be Thy name..."

Soon after tea, Uncle Tadeusz, my new Aunt Aniela and Papa arrived from Warsaw with some more bad news. Papa said that we were not going back to Warsaw because it was safer to stay here, in the village. He arranged for a wagon to bring our winter clothes and other belongings. I wondered what will happen to our school, but Mama said that when a country is fighting for its survival, there is no time for schooling. All evening Papa has been trying to get the wireless going but did not succeed. Tomorrow, he'll try to get to Warsaw and see what can be done about the set which is so vital to us just now. Please, Dear God, let our brave soldiers beat the nasty Germans.

2nd September 1939

PAPA and Mama, together with Aunt Aniela and Uncle Tadeusz, went to Warsaw early this morning. Uncle Tadeusz drove them in his Fiat soon after breakfast. We felt absolutely lost without the news. It is a pity that none of our neighbours has a wireless set. People have been calling at the house hoping to hear the latest news. All they knew about the war was what they read in the morning newspaper. Aunt Stefa and Irka were busy all day clarifying butter which will keep for hard times. I have been helping in the kitchen and feeding Danúska. She gets her special milk every two hours and her nappies have to be changed very often. All Danúska does is sleep, eat and wet her nappies. These three pursuits seem to suit her quite well. She cries only when she's hungry or wet. Today I made my first potato soup. Irka told me step by step how to make it. First, you peel and slice a few potatoes, carrots and onions. Then, you scrape two roots of Hamburg parsley. After that, you crush one clove of garlic. I, personally, prefer it without the garlic, but Irka said that I was in a minority. Finally, you put all the vegetables into a ready-made stock and boil it for half-an-hour, during which time salt and peppercorns are added. When the vegetables are soft, you add some sour cream and that's all. Although I am not very fond of soups, I ate my own concoction which wasn't too bad. Apart from the boys and Grandpa, everybody else (that is Irka and Aunt Stefa) said it was quite good. Pempela thought it was very good.

3rd September 1939

PAPA and Mama returned from Warsaw late last night together with our belongings. They hired a horse-drawn wagon and it took them several hours to get here. The roads were packed with soldiers and military vehicles. People in Warsaw are in high spirits and quite ready to fight. I wish I were in Warsaw too, because I can fight quite well when I set my mind to it. Papa brought a new battery, thank goodness, and is fiddling with the wireless at this very moment. Uncle Tadeusz and Aunt Aniela are coming back tomorrow or the day after because Uncle has been making arrangements for someone to mind his shop for him.

Magnificent news! England is going to thrash the Gerries in no time at all. Mr Chamberlain said that England has declared war against Germany. This welcome news came from the loudspeaker like a blessing from Heaven. I am so glad that we have some good friends abroad. Papa said that Great Britain is a mighty power with a strong Navy and Air Force. Everybody is greatly relieved and we celebrated with a drop of our special vintage wine. I shall have to learn some English because I know only one word, "Goodbye", and that's hardly enough to carry on a conversation with English soldiers. Papa said in three or four weeks they'll be here. When they come, I should like to thank them for helping us to beat Hitler but if I haven't learnt sufficient English to say so, I'll just have to hug them and they'll know what I mean.

4th September 1939

WE heard some heavy artillery fire. No-one seems to know where it was coming from. Grandpa took Mama and me to the market to get a stock of food but there was very little we could buy. The farmers are hanging on to their dairy produce and there were very few eggs left, and they have suddenly trebled in price. That also applies to wheat, flour and sugar. Anyway, we've managed to get a few kilogrammes of dry sausage and that will keep for many months. Mama went to see her friends and they sold her a large piece of pork belly and two kilogrammes of dripping. The Jewish shopkeepers are very frightened of Hitler and many have left their businesses and fled into the country. Grandpa promised to send them some vegetables. They were grateful and asked if we had a sufficient stock of oil and candles. It seems that Grandpa wants to buy anything he can lay his hands on. Grandpa knows from bitter experience that when there is a war, everything is in short supply.

Before sunset, Uncle Tadeusz and Aunt Aniela arrived bringing in a lot of valuable silver, glass, porcelain and other articles of sentimental value. Unfortunately, they also brought some bad news about our Baltic Corridor. The German Fourth Army has pushed through our defence lines. Uncle Tadeusz said that hundreds of Polish Cavalrymen lost their lives in a heroic battle. We were utterly sickened by this news. Grandpa suffered most. His empty eye-socket filled with tears. He blew his nose and went to the stable. Grandpa always goes to talk to Samson when things are bad.

5th September 1939

THE house has been like a beehive since early morning. Papa returned from a trip to the next village with a goat. Mama said that we shall certainly need the milk, and how clever it was of Papa to think of it. Papa, still oozing with pride, tied the goat to a small tree and waited for more compliments. Aunt Stefa took one look at Papa's acquisition and said that he'd be very lucky to get milk from a billy goat. After a certain amount of arguing and a thorough inspection of the billy-goat's private parts, Papa agreed to take him back. Aunt Stefa, gesticulating with both hands, started to explain to Papa the vital difference between a billy-goat and a nanny-goat. I think Papa in the end got the message, because when he returned, there was no more doubt that he had the right animal this time. He went into the kitchen and asked Irka for a bucket. Irka asked Papa whether he's done any milking before. I watched Papa from behind the grapevine. First, he gave the nanny a handful of weeds to eat in order to get her in the right mood. Then, he went to fetch an armchair from the dining room. It was a bit too high for the job, but Papa was not going to be put off by trifles. The goat said something to Papa which he took to mean more refreshments. Having pulled out half of the winter spinach bed, Papa settled finally in the armchair and started fondling the goat's udder. After some minutes of considerable concentration, Papa's forehead was wet with perspiration, but the bucket was as dry as a desert. Aunt Stefa came to investigate. She told him to squeeze as well as pull. Success, at last. However, the bucket was still dry but Papa's sleeves were saturated with goat's milk. "Into the bucket, you nit-wit," Aunt Stefa shouted, getting hysterics. Papa lost his sense of humour. He said something, which nearly curdled Nanny's milk and went to pour himself a glass of vodka. Papa is essentially a townsman and he appreciates only the country air.

51

6th September 1939

AFTER many years of idleness, the old bakery has been turned back to its proper use. Now that the horticultural students have gone, Mama has scrubbed the wooden table and mopped the floor. Grandpa put some twigs in the oven and lit them. Then he packed the whole oven with large sticks and logs and closed its door. The wood burned and heated the bricks nicely. Only Grandpa knows when the oven is ready for baking. Mama and Aunt Stefa were kneading the dough, which had been prepared in a large wooden pail from whole wheat flour. The kneading is the exhausting part. Both Mama and Aunt Stefa used their fists and pummelled the dough in rhythm: one, two, three, four. When they were almost out of breath, Grandpa pronounced that the dough had had enough beating. It was none the worse for its punishment. It glistened like putty. Mama covered the dough with a linen towel and left it to rise. The bakery was beautifully warm and in about three hours the dough nearly doubled in size. Then, Grandpa spread the red-hot charcoal evenly over the entire oven base and said it was time to shape the loaves. Mama blessed the dough and sprinkled the table-top with flour. She put her hands in warm water, and with wet hands she scooped out a big dollop of dough. She formed it into an oval loaf and put it on the floured table. Grandpa reminded Mama to make either seven or thirteen loaves. According to Grandpa, that's how his father baked bread and he saw no reason for changing the custom. When all the loaves were made, Grandpa scooped out the charcoal and one by one all seven loaves were popped into the oven. Grandpa closed the oven door and said that the bread should be ready in two hours. Sure enough it was. But Grandpa made absolutely certain that the bread was thoroughly baked by tapping each loaf. Mama's bread looked quite different from the shop bread and I said so. But Grandpa pointed out that it usually tastes better. He used to love eating crunchy crust with lots of butter, though that was when he had his own teeth. I asked Grandpa what happened to his teeth and he said that his brother Emil pulled the back ones with a pair of pliers, and the front ones just dropped out in sympathy.

7th September 1939

THE Germans are advancing towards Warsaw. The Polish Army suffered a heavy defeat on the border of East Prussia. Papa said that Hitler has bombed Britain. We are very worried. Uncle Tadeusz and the boys were busy burying all the family valuables in the shrubbery of our garden. Wooden boxes filled with cut glass, silver, best china and other heirlooms were wrapped in waterproof sheets and lowered into a deep hole. By lunchtime the hole was filled and levelled and some conifers were planted to disguise the spot. Uncle Tadeusz even laid some turf on top of the fresh soil. He praised the boys who worked wholeheartedly along with him. He gave them twenty groszy each, which is a lot of money. Uncle Tadeusz and his new wife are occupying Grandma's old room. I think Aunt Aniela felt somewhat uneasy. She very much hoped that they wouldn't have to share the room with Grandma's ghost. So, our "clever Dick", Jurek, could not allow the opportunity to pass without playing his favourite prank. Late in the evening, when Aunt Aniela and Uncle Tadeusz blew out their candle and settled down for the night, Jurek delivered himself outside their window. He was wearing Grandpa's white nightshirt and he painted his face with white chalk. Then, he made what he thought to be a "ghostly" noise, but Uncle Tadeusz recognised it as unmistakably a Jurek noise. While Jurek was performing outside their window, Uncle Tadeusz got up, wrapped himself in a white sheet and waited outside the front door for Jurek's return. There was an ear-piercing shriek followed by silence. Jurek nearly gave up his ghost. He fainted and Auntie Stefa had a real shock when she saw Uncle Tadeusz in his peculiar outfit, carrying white-faced Jurek clad in Grandpa's nightshirt. I think Jurek has learnt his lesson, but Auntie Stefa is still not on speaking terms with her brother.

8th September 1939

A HEAVY battle at Westerplatte ended in our surrender. Everybody is on edge. Warsaw is preparing to fight the Gerries till the very last drop of blood. Papa said that the government has been evacuated from Warsaw to Lublin. Only the mayor is left in the capital. Mr Starzynski appealed to Warsawvians on the wireless. We sat around the loudspeaker with long faces and lumps in our throats.

After lunch, Anton drove Mama, Aunt Stefa, Irka, Danúska and myself to church. Danúska in her christening robe, slept all the way. She looked like a little angel and was quite oblivious to the fact that she was the most important person of all, and was just about to be christened by Father Jakob. The countryside is different now. The fields are bare and some are already ploughed for winter sowing. Maples and chestnuts, making the most of their last opportunity, were sunning themselves in the autumn air. In the distance, we heard explosions and continuous gunfire. And yet, the landscape looked peaceful. The crows went about their business and the cows grazed contentedly by the roadside.

Danúska's full christian names are: Danuta, Johanna, Maria. Mama gave her a little silver medallion and a silver chain. Her godfather, Anton, gave her a new Bible. Aunt Stefa laid on a modest tea for the guests. We had ham sandwiches and sultana cake. Also some tea with either lemon or a drop of rum in it, according to one's taste. Nobody was jolly. People discussed the war and our chances of defending our country.

9th September 1939

A UNT Aniela has been giving us, the children, a lesson in English, just in case our friends manage to beat the Germans. She said that the first thing one should say when meeting any English person is, "How do you do?" The meaning being:

How is one getting along. But on no account should one start talking about one's progress. Instead, one must reply by repeating the question exactly, "How do you do?" Now, the English person also mustn't reply to your question, but must simply ignore it, assuming that the other person doesn't wish to hear the real answer. Aunt Aniela asked us whether it was clear. Tadek and Wojtek said it was perfectly clear but Jurek and I said it was not. So Aunt Aniela asked Tadek and Wojtek to do some acting. After considerable argument about who was going to be the Englishman and who the Pole, she decided that Tadek should be the Englishman because he knows some English already, such as "O.K." Having decided who was who, Tadek was sent outside to knock on the door. Aunt Aniela said, "Enter" but Tadek carried on knocking. So she explained to him that "Enter" means come in. Tadek came in, but now who was to be the first to say "How do you do?" Aunt Aniela said it did not matter, so Tadek went outside and once more knocked on the door. "Enter," said Aunt Aniela in her best English accent. Tadek and Wojtek confronted each other by saying simultaneously, "How do you do?" Of course, that was no good at all, but the third time they got it right at last. They just stood in the middle of the room, shaking hands and repeating like parrots, "How do you do?" Aunt Aniela was very pleased with their performance, but pointed out that in England people don't shake hands as freely as we do in Poland. The other greeting phrase frequently used was "How are you?" which means, how is one feeling? The answer to this question is quite different. In this case you don't repeat the question but there is a straightforward standard answer, "Very well, thank you," meaning, very healthy, thank you. Jurek at once wanted to know what happened if someone is feeling rotten. Aunt Aniela replied that being cussed would get him nowhere. She announced that lesson number one was at an end and we have to learn both greetings and both answers by heart.

10th September 1939

THE Russians have mobilised their troops and have moved towards the Polish border. We all know what that will mean to us. Warsaw is being continuously shelled. Grandpa's nerves are in a bad state. He can't sleep and he's lost his appetite. Uncle Tadeusz exchanged with Great-Uncle Emil a few sacks of potatoes for a small pig. Papa and I couldn't bear to see the pig killed so we went into a nearby wood to see if there were any mushrooms about. It was a lovely sunny day and I enjoyed being with Papa. Papa wants me to go to a university to study literature. I think I might manage that. I asked Papa what will happen if we lose the war. The important thing was, Papa replied, on no account to lose one's faith. Papa said that one can live without many things, even without food for many days, but never without hope. The loss of faith meant death, Papa said. We found no mushrooms, because the summer was too dry, but I'll remember about the faith as long as I live. I think I have the best Papa there ever was.

11th September 1939

WARSAW is fighting on. Day and night we hear explosions and heavy gun-fire. Papa managed to tune in to the BBC in London. It was very faint but Aunt Aniela feels pretty certain that British troops have landed on French soil. We are jolly glad to hear that. Papa grabbed Aunt Aniela and danced around the table. "The British are coming!" Aunt Aniela shouted, doing the Can-Can Polka. Everybody cheered up at once. We are very lucky to have Aunt Aniela with us otherwise we wouldn't be able to understand the news in English. When I went to the kitchen to tell Irka the good news, I noticed that she didn't look at all well. Her face was drawn and pale and her whole body had lost its plumpness. But she seemed cheerful and told me that Danúska has grown five centimetres since she was born. Irka measured her with a piece of string. I told Irka that any day now the British were coming, and how about a party for them. Irka said it was a pity that cherries were out of season. Cherry dumplings would have been just the thing to tickle the English soldiers' fancy. I reminded Irka about doughnuts with jam and we both agreed it was a good idea. I imagined myself with a big platter of doughnuts mingling among a crowd of English soldiers, wearing my yellow organza dress and a friendly smile. "How do you do?" I would say, and they would comment on my perfect English. Then, I would start to talk about the nice weather, not about the nasty war. Aunt Aniela said that in England it's a well-established custom to talk about the weather. I reminded her that they would be in Poland and we don't talk about the weather. But Aunt Aniela said it made no difference at all. Though, she agreed, that the topic of conversation should be the Polish weather as we knew nothing about the English weather. So, I've been practising my conversation with Wojtek. He was pretending to be the English soldier and I was pretending to be me. I said, in my best English accent, "Very good Polish weather." Wojtek replied, "Very good English weather," and that was that. Whether it was the topic, or our non-existent vocabulary, or both, the conversation just dropped dead. Sometimes I think I'll never learn English. I wish the English could speak Polish then we wouldn't have to talk about the weather or about "How do you do?"

12th September 1939

AUNT Aniela said that the English don't drink tea with lemon but with milk, the way we drink our coffee. Furthermore, she was doubtful if the goat's milk would do. Irka and I were bothered but Papa solved the problem. He said that Polish vodka was a much better bet than English tea. A substantial stock of vodka was a sensible thing to acquire. And he added that vodka, unlike milk, doesn't go off. But Mama said it did when

Papa was around, it just vanished into thin air. Well, vodka is rather volatile and I don't see why Papa should be blamed for it. Thank goodness, at least we'll know what to do when the English come to our village. Besides, Aunt Aniela should know exactly what to do to please the English soldiers. I am jolly glad she is here because she's been to London and she can look more English than the English do, she told us. It just shows how clever she is.

13th September 1939

I VERY much hope that the thirteenth is more unlucky to the Gerries than it is to us. Warsaw is fighting back. We can hear explosions by day and see the red sky at night. Several shells have landed in nearby fields. Uncle Tadeusz decided that we'd have to build a shelter at the bottom of the garden. He thinks that our house might become a target for Nazi tanks. Having chosen a suitable place, Uncle Tadeusz got everybody he could grab hold of, including his wife, and formed us into a platoon. As the Commander-in-chief, he handed each of us a spade and told us to dig while he went elsewhere. Being next to Aunt Aniela, I could see that she is not a digger. Every time I dug a hole, she filled it in. After half-an-hour, which seemed like two hours, Uncle Tadeusz returned to inspect the hole. He was not pleased with our progress, and he said so. It is Uncle's nature to call a spade a spade and he did not mince his words on this occasion either. He wanted to know whether I and Aunt Aniela were, by any chance, digging for worms. I said that I was not, but Aunt Aniela said that she would much rather dig for worms than for Uncle Tadeusz. And to emphasize what she'd just said, she aimed her spade at the ground, but landed it on Uncle's foot. Uncle yelled and hobbled back towards the house in a huff. Aunt Aniela ran after him begging his forgiveness. We all agreed that it was a bad day for digging the shelter. We sank our spades in the ground and followed the Chief.

14th September 1939

TODAY, Aunt Aniela has been teaching us to sing a truly English song called *I'll Take the High Road*. She feels it would be only right and proper to greet our allies with a song in their own tongue. She knows two songs in English. One is about the "High Road" and the other one is about a "Beautiful Dreamer". I like the one about the dreamer. It has such a sweet tune. I nearly cried when I heard Aunt Aniela singing it to us. The lyric is beautiful too, though I couldn't understand a word of it. However, Aunt Aniela thinks that the song about the road should be more appropriate. We all gathered around the piano and had to learn the tune first. Aunt Aniela told us to "la, la" while she played the tune with one hand and directed us with the other. She said that Papa was the most musical one among our lot. I don't think Uncle Tadeusz liked that. Each time Papa's "la , las" lilted across the room, Uncle Tadeusz's "la, las" nearly blasted our eardrums. He has a powerful voice but, unfortunately, he can't sing in tune. Aunt Stefa nicknamed him the Great Caruso. After that we had a job to tear him away from the piano. Uncle Tadeusz never does things by halves and Aunt Aniela realised too late that it was a mistake to encourage her husband's vocal cords. She said that we, the children, will have to copy out the lyrics in English during our next lesson.

15th September 1939

IT'S been a real autumn day. The sun filtered through red and yellow acers as if reflecting the blood and fire from the Polish battlefields. From morning till dusk we've heard guns and rumblings echoing across the sky. The people of Warsaw are defending their homes and their honour. There was some distressing news on the wireless. Hitler's Army has broken through and captured Gdynia. Grandpa is praying all the time, his fingers clutching the rosary and his lips whispering endlessly "Hail Mary". Irka has a bad chest. She's been coughing a lot. Every day I take little Danúska for a walk. Our next-door-but-one neighbour lent Irka an old pram. Danúska loves her rides. I've been singing to her our English song and she knew it was like nothing she's heard so far. Her expression turned into a grin which, of course, could have been the result of something else. Danúska's eyes are getting more blue and her hair has a tinge of copper. She is a little beauty all right.

Mama and Aunt Stefa have been pickling herrings. It's a messy and a smelly job and I tried to stay clear of the kitchen.

16th September 1939

SOME good news today. The Germans have been repulsed on the Western Front. Our hopes rose and with them our moods improved. Uncle Tadeusz started to tease Mama and Aunt Stefa. He said that Mama puts on weight in front whereas Aunt Stefa does at the back, and it was quite out of character for identical twins to behave in such a contrary way. Aunt Stefa replied that he was a fine one to talk about other people's figures. Has he, meaning Uncle, by any chance, seen his own paunch? Uncle Tadeusz said he had, and it was not without purpose. Putting on weight around the middle kept him well balanced. Mama said that he was unbalanced because his head was too big. Everybody laughed, including Grandpa. Even Pempela wagged her tail. It was just like before the war. Mama made some cheese from the goat's milk. It looked delicious but nobody wanted to eat it. People just passed the cheese around and it came back to Mama untouched. She said it was the last time she was going to take the trouble to make cheese. Uncle Tadeusz, having made a sigh of relief, handed Mama pencil and paper and asked her to put it in writing. Everyone burst out laughing again, as if making the most of it before the next onset of doom.

18th September 1939

THE shelter is ready. Uncle Tadeusz, having banished every female from the site, harnessed men to finish the job. Our shelter consists of a large hole in the ground which is lined with straw. The roof is made of logs, straw and earth. Papa said it was as depressing as a graveyard and a proper death-trap. And he, for one, won't be risking his neck by going in there. Uncle Tadeusz said that Papa might change his mind when a shell lands in his bed. Papa replied that he would much rather sleep with a shell than in Uncle's shelter. I said that I wanted to stay in the house too, but Mama ticked me off and said that I'll have to do what she says and not what I want to do. I felt cross with Mama and didn't like her just then. After ten-thirty in the evening, when the gun-fire intensified its rage, and when the moon climbed up the blue-black sky, we packed ourselves on the straw in the shelter like sardines. There was practically no room to lie down and not much air to breathe. The onion soup from supper was not a good idea, pointed out Uncle Tadeusz. At that moment he must have envied Papa, though he didn't say so. I asked Mama whether I could go back to my bed but she said "No", and in such a funny tone of voice that I did not dare to ask her again. Jurek complained that he couldn't breathe and Aunt Stefa told him to do without breathing. Every time somebody moved, a trickle of sand came down from the roof. Aunt Aniela said she felt like a mummy without having the advantage of being embalmed. Every quarter-of-an-hour somebody asked what was the time. By three in the morning, the atmosphere in the shelter got so heavy that if we'd stayed there a minute longer we would have suffocated. Aunt Aniela scrambled out first, saying that she'd much rather be blown to bits by a bullet than be poisoned by bad onions. We all followed, thankful for her courage. Mama could hardly stand up. She had cramp in one leg and pins and needles in the other. We toddled off to the house, truly grateful for having a real roof over our heads and real beds to sleep in. Last night was the first time we used the garden shelter and it could well be the last. Very likely Uncle Tadeusz did not think much of his own architecture either, for he was just as pleased to get out of it.

19th September 1939

WE are overwhelmed with sorrow. Polish resistance has collapsed. The Russians and the Germans have met near Brest Litovsk. Warsaw is on its last legs. Papa said that they are short of ammunition and food. The German propaganda is pouring in from every wavelength. Papa's been trying to get the BBC on his secret wireless set which is somewhere in the attic. Papa often goes up there with Aunt Aniela. He fiddles with the knobs and she takes everything down. Then Tadek and Wojtek distribute the news around the village.

This afternoon, Father Jakob called to see how we are getting on. Grandpa was full of indignation about God allowing such injustice to prevail on Polish soil. Father Jakob had to stop Grandpa before he said something terrible. When Grandpa gets going and when he's het up no-one is safe, not even God. Having soothed Grandpa's nerves, Father Jakob said that we, the children of God, are not here to question His wisdom but to pray for help and peace. Grandpa said that's exactly what he's been doing and a lot of good it did. Father Jakob replied that God has been awfully busy lately with everybody praying at the same time. Grandpa nodded and agreed that it must be sheer hell in Heaven, just now. Father Jakob's words do to Grandpa's soul what Mama's pancakes do to Father Jakob's stomach. Some pancakes with cheese and sultanas were what we had for tea today. It was the goat's cheese that Mama was determined not to waste. She crumbled it, added some eggs and sugar, a few sultanas and a few drops of vanilla essence. Mama's culinary skill transformed the cheese so completely that even our nanny-goat wouldn't recognise her own product. Mama winked at me when everyone praised the pancakes, but I said nothing.

20th September 1939

GREAT-UNCLE Emil came to see Grandpa to discuss the matter of guns and other weapons in the village. Grandpa suggested hiding them under the hay in the barn. But Uncle Tadeusz pointed out that it was the first place the Germans would search. He said the safest place for all weapons was underground. Later in the morning, Great-Uncle Emil and Anton brought in at least a dozen different guns and buried them somewhere in the garden. I only hope Uncle Tadeusz can remember what is buried where.

Anton heard from a friend that he had met a shepherd who had seen a German soldier near Zegrze. That's only three kilometres from us. So I went to a nearby field to see if I could spot any German soldiers. I saw nothing but heard enough to last me a long time. When I got about three hundred metres from the house, I heard bullets whistling around me. At first I didn't realise what was happening, until I saw puffs of dust in the road. Someone was shooting at me. Immediately I lay down on the ground, too petrified to move. My heart was thumping like mad. After a while the shooting stopped. I didn't know what to do. The Germans must be quite near, I reckoned. I started to crawl, almost slithering like a grass snake. My dress, my knees and my hands were covered in dust. After several minutes I heard a cow mooing. A bullet had gone through her hind leg. Blood was pouring down and the poor beast was in agony. By then I was really scared. I got up and ran as fast as I could. When I got to the house, filthy and out of breath, Mama was furious with me. Before I had the chance to explain what had happened she spanked me. I went to my room and cried and cried. But then I remembered the poor injured cow. So I went to tell Grandpa about it. He praised me and said it was an act of God that I saw the incident, otherwise the cow, belonging to Anton's sister-in-law, might have bled to death. At once Anton went to the cow with his first-aid kit. Afterwards, when Mama helped me to change and wash, I think she was sorry

63

for spanking me so hastily for she hugged and kissed me and said that it was a silly thing to do. Papa was quite worried when he learnt how near the Germans are. He went up to the attic to hide the wireless set. For the time being, Papa put it underneath a pile of dirty washing. After tea, Uncle Tadeusz went to the attic and knocked several bricks out of the chimney stack and built a handy hideout for the wireless on the side facing the roof. It was a removable panel and it is almost invisible. Uncle Tadeusz said it was all right so long as no-one lit the fire in the south side of the house.

21st September 1939

OUR capital is on fire. At night we can see the sky stained with smoke and flame. The guns have died down. German troops have surrounded Warsaw almost completely. Papa says it's only a matter of days. We feel thoroughly dejected, forsaken by justice. Why, oh why, are the Nazis winning the war?

22nd September 1939

IT'S Tadek's birthday today. He's sixteen, which is quite grown-up. Wojtek is fourteen-and-a-half and Jurek is thirteen. Thirteen is a bad number altogether and that probably accounts for Jurek's peculiar behaviour. Though he's been a bit better lately, touch wood. The boys have to help now on the small-holding, announced Uncle Tadeusz, and I have to help around the house. Well, I do, sometimes. Mama said that my cleaning is something I should be least proud of. She caught me sweeping dirt under the carpet. As a penance, I had to clean the windows. Cleaning windows is the worst job I've done so far, that is except for scrubbing the privy seat. Uncle Tadeusz is keen that everyone should work. Only Pempela has been jolly lucky to have got off scot-free, so far. Sometimes the boys hide when Uncle Tadeusz wants them to work in the garden. To Uncle Tadeusz working is as necessary as praying is to Grandpa, and once Uncle said that praying was a waste of time. Grandpa banged his rosary on the table and said there would be no work for Uncle if God did not answer Grandpa's prayers. After that, Uncle never argued with Grandpa. Today, Uncle Tadeusz has been busy making a headstone for Grandma's grave. Wojtek has made a small sculpture of Jesus's head from chalk and Uncle used that to make a moulded impression on a concrete cross, while the cement was still soft. The cross looked amazingly professional and everyone praised Wojtek for being so clever. Pempela also came to admire the monument and left a permanent imprint of her paw in the cement. Fortunately, Uncle Tadeusz didn't notice it, and I hope Grandma won't object to having a doggy token of affection. Though little Gabriel's paw-print might have pleased Grandma even more.

24th September 1939

THIS morning, Uncle Tadeusz, the boys, Grandpa and myself drove to the cemetery. The cross is not quite dry but Uncle Tadeusz said it would have to do, as we can't tell what tomorrow might bring. Mama gave me a bunch of roses to put on Grandma's grave. The cemetery seemed quite deserted, not a soul in sight. The chestnuts and maples looked like half-bare skeletons. And the dead leaves underfoot had nothing to remind one of their recent autumn glory. Uncle said that people can't bear to visit a cemetery when their own lives are threatened. He was right because I didn't like being there. I just wanted to get home and Samson felt the same. He trotted back without any prompting from Grandpa's whip.

25th September 1939

NOTHING but bad news. People are prepared for the worst to happen. A convoy of German troops on the main road to Warsaw has been reported by one villager. Grandpa is in a state of continuous anxiety. Mama is worried about his health. She's been brewing a herbal potion for his nerves. The odour of valerian pervaded the whole house and Papa said that anyone who can survive its wicked smell can survive anything. Mama made the brew in a jug and insisted that Grandpa should drink the lot. The effect was indisputable. Grandpa was flat out for the rest of the day. Mama got worried and wondered whether she'd cured him too much, and wanted to call the doctor. But Uncle Tadeusz said that, before getting better, it was quite natural for anyone to pass through a bad patch. Mama was not at all convinced, but she agreed that, at least, Grandpa's nerves were having a rest. After several hours, Grandpa was still passing through his bad patch. He remained in bed, sleeping it off, for two days. When the Germans came, Grandpa was beyond any fear, but the rest of us, quite literally, shivered in our boots. A full lorry-load of Gerries spilled out at our gate at the crack of dawn. They bashed on the front door, nearly knocking Uncle Tadeusz down, and rampaging through the house like a torrent of hoodlums. With their rifles at the ready, they poked and probed at anything and everything. Presumably, having found nothing they were looking for, they departed, leaving everybody alive, thank the Lord, but the house in a dreadful mess. After the visitation we all felt like a drop of Mama's valerian.

26th September 1939

BOROWA-GÓRA is swarming with Gerries. There are at least two soldiers for every villager. Their uniforms are greenish-blue, and they are wearing black, knee-length boots. Some have helmets on their heads, others just forage caps, but all carry pistols hanging from their belts. The amazing part is that they feel quite at home in our village. They know exactly where to find food or water, how many men there are available for labour, and how many horses and carts there are at hand. They seem to know everything, though none, as far as I know, can speak Polish. Our German language is virtually non-existent. Uncle Tadeusz has a smattering of it and Aunt Aniela finds it not too difficult to guess what they say, German being somewhat similar to English. Though Papa feels it's useful to know "*nicht verstehen*". So far, Herr Kommandant von Klein has only been wanting food, and he didn't ask for it, he just helped himself. Our cellar seems to have great fascination for Herr Kommandant. Fortunately, Mama and Aunt Stefa managed to smuggle out some of our precious preserves before they disappeared. Herr Kommandant set up his headquarters in the other house belonging to Grandpa which is usually let to holidaymakers, and which is situated near the main road to Warsaw. Thank goodness it's some distance from our house, and Papa still might be able to listen to an occasional news bulletin on his secret wireless.

27th September 1939

GREAT-UNCLE Emil is furious with the Gerries because they've pinched his best laying pullet. Furthermore, they told Anton's wife to pluck and roast the chicken for their supper. Anton's wife felt like seasoning it with arsenic instead of salt. Alas, she said, she didn't have anything like that handy in her kitchen.

Papa said that Warsaw is about to capitulate. It's a matter not even of days, but hours. Our morale is very low. I have to help every day in the kitchen because Irka isn't feeling too well. Aunt Stefa said that she could be sickening for her sweetheart. The only person who loses neither sleep nor appetite over our plight is Danúska. She's a chubby little baby and no trouble at all. Even Grandpa admits that she's as good as gold. I am knitting a blanket for Danúska's cot. Mama showed me how to use up odd bits of wool. I knit them into squares and Mama joins them with a crochet hook. I've done five squares so far. It takes me about two days to knit one square but Mama says that in time my knitting will become faster. I hope so too, otherwise poor Danúska would have to wait an awful long time for her blanket.

28th September 1939

WARSAW surrendered yesterday. Mr Starzynski, the city mayor, has been shot by the Nazis. We feel appalled by this barbaric act. Grandpa took it very badly and asked for another dose of Mama's brew but she was somewhat reluctant to give it to him. Instead, Papa mixed him a vodka cocktail. Grandpa drank two glasses at once and a third one more leisurely. After that, he felt much better. So much so, that he went to see Herr Kommandant in his new headquarters and told him to clear out. Luckily for all of us, and even more so for Grandpa, Herr Kommandant had no idea what Grandpa was on about. Uncle Tadeusz, having learnt what Grandpa was up to, went to fetch him, explaining to the German commander that his father was suffering from mental aberration. Mama put Grandpa to bed and blamed Papa for everything. She said that vodka must have been invented by the devil himself, because it brings misery to so many. And pleasure to millions, pointed out Papa. Mama argued that all Papa does is to seek pleasure. To which Papa replied that he saw nothing wrong in enjoying himself. They argued for at least half-an-hour, by which time Grandpa got sober and Mama felt better for having made Papa miserable.

29th September 1939

UNCLE Tadeusz has been trying to get to Warsaw but without any luck. The city is surrounded by German troops and no-one from the inside or the outside is allowed to cross the border. Apparently, the people of Warsaw are carrying on with their work as usual, in spite of the fact that many buildings have been completely destroyed, or burned down. Uncle is furious with the Gerries. He wants to know what has happened to his shops in Warsaw. The frontier between the city on the south side and the rest of the country is along the river Bug and the customs post, set up by the Germans, is at Zegrze. Uncle Tadeusz drove his Fiat as far as the bridge and there he was stopped. He had to show his credentials, the number of his car was taken, together with his name and address. At one stage, Uncle thought they would detain him. Luckily, he was released and lost no time driving back home as fast as he could. Gradually, we are learning to keep quiet and inconspicuous, but always hoping that tomorrow will bring a brighter outlook.

30th September 1939

AUNT Aniela has been summoned to cook dinners for Herr Kommandant at his headquarters in Grandpa's other house. Uncle Tadeusz tried to explain that his wife knew very little about cooking and suggested that Irka might suit him better. But the answer was no. Herr Kommandant knows exactly what he likes and Aunt Aniela was his choice. So she reported at his office just after six and was told to prepare pork chops, sauerkraut and potatoes for his supper. Aunt Aniela is as good at cooking as she is at digging, which amounts to very little. Not many people could produce a burnt glass of tea. Well, Aunt Aniela can, I know, because I've sampled it. Although we all felt sorry for her, Irka and I could not help giggling at the unlikely finesse of the cordon bleu meal prepared by Aunt Aniela. It serves Herr Kommandant right, and with a little bit of luck he might even choke.

1st October 1939

THANK goodness Aunt Aniela has been sacked from her job as cook to Herr Kommandant. The supper she prepared for him was so terrible that even his dog wouldn't touch it. Papa said that there is virtue in not being too expert in too many things, and Aunt Aniela's case was a good example. However, the joy over Aunt Aniela's dismissal was marred by the confiscation of Uncle's Fiat. Four soldiers came to claim the car and as no-one was able to start the engine, they towed it away. Uncle Tadeusz looked so down-hearted that we felt very sorry for him. Bravely, he said it did not matter so long as our family stayed together. And the best way to stay sane is to keep busy. He and Papa brought into the kitchen a huge basket filled with cabbages for us to preserve for winter. Everybody joined in as it is a big job. The cabbages were halved and the stalks removed. Then they were shredded finely. Mama and Aunt Stefa are best at shredding cabbage because they've done it every year. Uncle Tadeusz brought in a large barrel which Irka scrubbed using boiling water. Mama put first a layer of the shredded cabbage, salted it thoroughly, and Papa pressed it with a wooden pestle until the juice covered the leaves. We tried to sing some patriotic songs, but that didn't come off, so Grandpa told us his favourite story. Everyone has heard it at least twice, but Grandpa loves telling it and we didn't like to deny him that pleasure. When Grandpa was a young boy, he went into a nearby wood which belonged to the Radziwil family. It was two days before Christmas and Grandpa went to cut a fir tree. He put a saw and an axe on his sledge and battled through several snowdrifts until he found a nice shapely Christmas tree. As he was reaching for the saw, he caught a glimpse of a big dog emerging from behind the bushes. A pair of red eyes were staring from the depth of his shaggy head. Grandpa realised in a flash that those eyes were not the eyes of a dog. It was a wolf gloating at his prospects of a supper. Grandpa stood petrified. But as the fear let go of his limbs, he snatched the axe and looked around him. The wolf seized the moment of Grandpa's indecision and leapt forward. Grandpa threw his hat and ran towards the nearest tree. The wolf went for the hat and Grandpa, with the help of the axe, managed to climb an old oak. The wolf, having torn the hat into shreds, started snarling and howling at Grandpa. After a couple of hours, Grandpa was numbed with cold but that beastly animal was still there, keeping its vigil under the tree. The sun went down and the sickle of the moon appeared in the sky. Grandpa was getting really worried. He tried shouting at the wolf and reciting his prayers until his lips became quite stiff. In the middle of the night, when Grandpa was half-frozen and resigned to his fate, he heard a human voice. His brothers, Emil and Adam, were looking for him. The wolf got scared and ran off. Grandpa, frozen to the bone, was at last rescued from his frightening ordeal.

Befitting the story, we made the appropriate comments and Grandpa was happy, and the barrel was full of cabbage. Uncle Tadeusz said that storing the barrel in the cellar was as safe as keeping sugar lumps in Samson's mouth. The Gerries would sniff out their favourite food in no time. A bedroom was a better place, he suggested. But whose bedroom, was the question. When cabbage begins to ferment, it pongs to high Heaven. We drew lots. And who should draw the one marked with a cross? Yes, Uncle Tadeusz himself. We laughed for ten minutes at least, and it did us good.

3rd October 1939

A GERMAN soldier shot little Gabriel. We are sickened at this callous act of violence. The soldier came to tell us to report for potato picking next week. Gabriel doesn't like strangers and he could not resist nipping his leg. The soldier pulled out his revolver and shot Gabriel on the spot. The dog died instantly. Mama and Aunt Stefa are very upset. Uncle Tadeusz told Tadek

71

to bury Gabriel somewhere in the garden. We wrapped him in a clean cloth and put him in a little coffin which Wojtek made from bits of wood. On the headstone, we inscribed the words: "Here lies little angel Gabriel who bit the big devil".

5th October 1939

IRKA'S been in bed for two days. She has a nasty cough and a sore chest. The midwife from the next village came to massage her chest and set some *banki* on her back. Irka had to lie on her tummy while Mrs Luta placed glass cups on Irka's bare back. First, Mrs Luta lit a candle. Then she poured a few drops of methylated spirit on a dish. She took a knitting needle, wound some cotton-wool around one end, making a small swab. She dipped the swab in the meths and lit it. Holding the lighted swab with one hand, Mrs Luta placed the cup over the flame in order to warm up the air inside it, and then she stuck it on Irka's back. With a remarkable swiftness, she stuck twenty cups altogether. The flesh inside the cup rose up in pink blisters. I have never seen anything like it and was very concerned for Irka, but she said it did not hurt at all. Mrs Luta pronounced that the *banki* would get the circulation going and it would do Irka a world of good. After twenty minutes, when Irka's back began to look as if it were covered with slices of red tomatoes, Mrs Luta decided that the *banki* had done their trick. She pulled them off, one by one. It sounded like corks being pulled out of champagne bottles. Now Irka moaned quite unashamedly and I wondered how one could put up with such a deadly cure. Irka's tormented back was then brushed with olive oil and wrapped in a flannel. Mrs Luta collected her three zloty from Mama and said that Irka should be as right as rain within a couple of days. Mama gave Irka a glass of goat's milk with garlic and honey and, at last, she was left in peace. I sincerely hope I'll never get chest trouble.

72

8th October 1939

EVERYONE from our household, with the exclusion of Grandpa, Samson and Pempela had to report for potato harvesting in Jadwisin, the next village, on a farm which belonged to the Radziwil family. Now it seems to belong to the Gerries, like everything else. Not only our household, but most of the inhabitants of Borowa-Góra were summoned to work in the fields. There are an awful lot of soldiers and they need an awful lot of food. The confiscation of crops from our fields presents no problem to the Gerries. It comes to them as easily and as naturally as invading our country. At eight in the morning, Grandpa harnessed Samson to the cart and we scrambled onto it, wearing boots and working clothes and looking just right for the job. Though Papa, at first, appeared in his bowler, but Uncle Tadeusz lent him his bee-keeping hat. It sank over Papa's ears and I wondered if he would be able to see what he was doing. But Papa did not seem to worry unduly. Grandpa unloaded us at the potato field exactly at nine-thirty and, having warned us not to work too hard, he said he'd be back to fetch us for lunch. Presently, other people arrived for work, and a German soldier came as well to keep an eye on us, no doubt. No-one appeared to be down in the dumps, on the contrary, people were laughing and treating the enforced labour as a joke. A German mechanical digger, driven by another soldier, turned from the road into the field. Our task was to pick the potatoes and put them into big baskets. However, Uncle Tadeusz had a much better idea. He suggested, as quietly and as inconspicuously as it were possible under the circumstances, that some of the spuds should be put in a nearby ditch. Thus we laboured as fast as we could, tipping one basket onto a potato pile, and two baskets into the ditch. In spite of our legs, which were aching, and our backs, which were nearly breaking, we sang as we laboured along. But it was so good when, at last, our work was at an end and dear Samson came to fetch us back.

9th October 1939

IN the early hours of this morning, before the light had had the chance to dilute the night, Uncle Tadeusz and several other people from the village went to bring the potatoes from the ditch. Thanks to Uncle's ingenuity, there should be no shortage of potatoes this winter. To celebrate our modest victory over the Gerries we had some potato pancakes for dinner. They are delicious, but must be eaten while hot. So we decided to have our feast on the kitchen table. First, we peeled and grated at least two dozen of the largest spuds we could find. Then Mama mixed in an equal number of tablespoons of self-raising flour. She added some salt and spooned the mixture into our largest frying pan containing hot oil. She fried the flat cakes on both sides until they were golden brown. Needless to say, we ate them faster than Mama could fry them. If ever there was a case where hell's labour turned into sheer heaven, it must have been through the magic of the potato pancake. That's what Papa said, as he dug his teeth into his third helping.

11th October 1939

YESTERDAY we went to Serock to be fingerprinted at the German police station. We are going to be issued with identity cards which every Pole will have to carry with him wherever he goes, including the privy I suppose.

Papa has difficulty in getting news on his secret wireless. We don't know how the British are getting on. Today we've been collecting some cones and firewood from a nearby wood. Uncle Tadeusz feels that there might be a shortage of coal and we'd better be prepared for the worst. To our surprise and delight we found quite a lot of edible toadstools. After the recent rain, they sprang up all over the woodland. The disagreeable part about toadstools is that they are so messy to prepare. However, once that was accomplished the end result was rewarding and, I might add, entirely due to Mama. She stewed them first and then mixed them with scrambled eggs. We had them for tea with bread and butter. Mama is certainly the best cook in our family. Aunt Stefa is also good, but in Mama's case, she loves cooking even better than eating. I don't think I shall ever be as good at cooking as Mama is because I prefer eating every time.

Pempela's been stung by a wasp. She's been in real agony. I put some bicarbonate on the swollen part of her face and told her not to stick her nose into wasps' nests. The trouble with Pempela is that she is always very curious and sometimes she has to pay the penalty for her incessant nosiness. But then, she is unusually intelligent and she likes to find out things for herself. If Pempela were a human being she'd be a genius. As it is, her intellect seldom, if ever, impresses anyone among her own kind, or among our kind for that matter. It seems to me that on four, a dog hardly has a leg to stand on.

14th October 1939

THE swallows departed earlier than usual and Grandpa said that we might be heading for a hard winter. Heaven forbid, said Papa, who hates snow and ice even more than the cat Rasputin from next door. Papa gets cold feet just by looking at snow. I, on the other hand, adore winter. Sledging and skating are my favourite games, but just walking in deep snow is great fun too. Aunt Aniela is busy knitting warm pullovers and earmuffs for the boys and for Uncle Tadeusz. She got some thick wool from her friend in Serock. In the evenings we usually sit around the dining table and get on with our hobbies. Aunt Aniela and I knit. Mama and Aunt Stefa sew. Tadek and Jurek play draughts and squabble. Wojtek either paints or draws caricatures of everybody. Papa and Uncle Tadeusz smoke cigarettes and discuss politics. Grandpa sits in his armchair and snoozes. Pempela also enjoys her forty winks before having a proper sleep. Irka likes reading when she has a spare moment and Danúska likes sucking

75

her fingers when she is awake. We have a big oil lamp in the middle of the table, which illuminates the room quite well and it also warms up the room. October evenings are chilly and it is cosy to sit around the table and listen to the hissing of the burning wick. When the oil gets low it is time for bed.

16th October 1939

IRKA is much better. Whether it was due to Mrs Luta's *banki* or Irka's natural process of recovery one could argue. And sure enough, they did. Aunt Aniela said that *banki* were not far off from witch-doctoring and should be taken with a pinch of salt. But Aunt Stefa replied that it is far better to do something than nothing. And, furthermore, if people believed in *banki* it was all to the good. Aunt Aniela said that some people are prepared to believe that standing on their heads does them good. But those with their feet firmly on the ground laugh at the very idea. At that point in the conversation, Aunt Stefa walked out, shutting the door firmly and loudly behind her. That ended the argument all right, but it also started a spell of sulking. Aunt Stefa finds it easy to sulk with difficult and disagreeable people. That's why she couldn't get on with her ex-husband. Aunt Stefa said that they usually argued when he was drunk and they weren't on speaking terms when he was sober. I hope that Aunt Stefa and Aunt Aniela will soon be friends again.

19th October 1939

WOJTEK has made a model aeroplane which actually flies. It is of his own design and Papa said it is quite ingenious. Wojtek used a bamboo cane which he split into half-centimetre strips. He bent the bamboo strips to shape over a candle-flame, thus forming the framework for the wings and the fuselage. He covered the whole framework with parchment paper using glue. The propeller and the wheels Wojtek carved out from some very light wood. Instead of an engine, he used a piece of rubber cut out of an old tyre's inner tube, which he attached to the propeller. The model is about half-a-metre in length and about the same in the wingspan. It has the Polish emblem painted in red and white on the wings and the tail. We all agree that Wojtek's aeroplane looks quite real, but will it fly? We waited, watching Wojtek winding the propeller. Jurek started the count-down. On the word "go", Wojtek released the propeller. The model jerked as if in an epileptic fit and suddenly rose to a height of about two metres and flew the full length of our concrete terrace. We were amazed, because no-one really expected it to fly, not even Wojtek himself. The unfortunate part was that, on landing, it crashed down and damaged its propeller. Nevertheless, it was quite an achievement and Papa was very proud of our Wojtek. He said that Wojtek is going to be a Leonardo da Vinci the Second.

22nd October 1939

THERE are not so many Gerries about our village now. Uncle Tadeusz managed to smuggle himself across the river to Warsaw. A friend of his took him across during the night in a small boat. Uncle Tadeusz said it was a nerve-racking experience but necessary, as far as he was concerned. For Uncle Tadeusz was not only relieved to see that his shops have suffered no excessive damage, but also was able to hide many of his valuable items. He used the cellar of his shop in Marszalkowska Street. He dug a hole in the cellar and buried the stuff there. Apparently the people of Warsaw are bearing up under the German occupation as well as can be expected. There is already a well organised resistance working underground, so to speak. However, there is a shortage of food, fuel and other essentials to a greater extent than in our village. Uncle Tadeusz said that we are better off staying in Borowa-Góra. Warsaw also suffered considerable damage to power stations and many tram-lines are out of action. The electricity and gas are available for only two hours each evening. Uncle Tadeusz also managed to let his flat, as well as ours, to his clients. They will keep an eye on our homes, as both flats have been broken into. As far as Uncle could see, only some of the carpets are missing, but the furniture is still there. Uncle stayed in Warsaw only one night and on the following night the same friend brought him back. The rowing trips across the river Bug can be accomplished successfully only on moonless nights. There are two places where, in comparative safety, such smuggling can take place. However, the time of crossing has to coincide with the German patrol change and it is a tricky business. Uncle Tadeusz had to lie down in the boat and he said it was an unforgettable experience.

25th October 1939

I ASKED Father Jakob yesterday if it were a sin to be nasty to the Gerries. Father Jakob scratched his head and said that under normal circumstances it would be a sin. But, taking into consideration the fact that we are at war, or, to be more precise, the Germans are occupying our country, God probably would be prepared to give us some sort of dispensation. Then I asked him, even if I were to kill a German, would I not end up in Hell? Father Jakob said that in self-defence killing is permissible, but not premeditated killing. He wanted to know whether I followed him and I said that I did, which is a lie, because I didn't. In actual fact, the more I think about the sin of killing the less I understand the whole business. To me, a killed man, for whatever reason, is a dead man, and to him surely it doesn't matter why he had died? His only worry is that he's dead and he can't do anything about it. Then I asked Papa if he would consider pinching spuds from the Gerries were a sin. Papa said it was most certainly not. He explained it to me like this: suppose a burglar stole my doll and I pinched it back. That wouldn't be stealing because the doll belonged to me in the first place. The same with the Germans. They have no right to be here. It is they who are the thieves. They are taking our crops from our fields and, on top of this, they are forcing us to work for them. Papa said it was a triple sin. I can always understand Papa and I hope God will remember to give the Gerries three bad marks.

27th October 1939

AFTER a horrible lunch, which consisted of vegetable soup with floating Hamburg parsley, we had a jolly good meal this evening. *Pierogi* are very tasty, although they take a considerable time to prepare. First, Mama minced some cooked beef and onions while Irka kneaded the noodle-like pastry. She rolled it very, very thin and then cut it out with a glass into lots and lots of circles. Using a teaspoon, Mama put some minced meat onto one half-circle and folded the other half over. She sealed the edges and made a decorative pattern by folding and twisting the pastry all along the curved side. Mama's *pierogi* looked very dainty and no-one can make them the way Mama does. Irka popped the *pierogi* into boiling water and when they were cooked we ate them with melted butter. Everybody enjoyed the meal and Mama was so full of praise that she hadn't much room for eating. I gave one to Pempela when Mama wasn't looking and she just swallowed it, without due regard for its exquisite flavour. I don't think our Pempela is much of a gourmet. But then, all intellectual creatures are far more preoccupied with thoughts rather than with stomachs.

29th October 1939

TODAY Papa shut himself in his room. He closed all the windows and even blocked the keyhole, because it's been a privy day. Tadek and Uncle Tadeusz emptied its contents onto the vegetable patch and it stinks to high heaven. Papa doesn't enjoy that sort of country air, neither do I. Only Pempela and Uncle Tadeusz think it's a lovely pong. Uncle has even been complaining that the deposits were far below the usual quota. Tomorrow they're going to plough it in, thank goodness.

1st November 1939

GRANDPA has a cyst on his foot and it is painful when he walks. Aunt Stefa said that he has to go and see the doctor. After some argument, Grandpa reluctantly gave in. The argument started all over again when Auntie brought in a bowl of hot water for Grandpa to wash his feet. He wanted to wash only one foot, the poorly one. And Aunt Stefa insisted that he should wash them both just in case the doctor wanted to look at the other foot. Grandpa grumbled that washing two feet, when one would do, was a waste of good soap and a waste of time. Auntie pointed out that since Grandpa had plenty of both, the waste would be negligible and the sooner Grandpa took the bowl and put his foot in it, the better it would be for everyone. In the end Grandpa did what he was told and gave his tootsies a proper treat. They needed it desperately, by the look of the water. In fact, Grandpa's poorly foot got much better straight away. The cyst had disappeared altogether. Grandpa said that it was a miracle, and Auntie said that he should try to perform this miracle more often.

80

2nd November 1939

LAST night Irka saw Grandma's ghost. She said she was sure it was Grandma because the ghost was wearing a dress split at the back. Irka could have been right because, for one thing, it's the proper time for ghosts to wander about around All Soul's Day, and for another, Grandma hasn't been since she's been gone, and that is more than three months. Irka said she was not frightened at all. She just watched Grandma coming through the door, without opening it, of course, and lifting the lids of two saucepans as if she were looking for some food or a drink. I didn't know ghosts got hungry, but then I haven't seen one yet. Grandma said nothing, though Irka did say "Good evening", but she received no answer. That made her convinced that it was a ghost because an earthly person would have replied. I suggested that perhaps last night wasn't a good night for Grandma. Otherwise she wouldn't have chosen to come down to earth from a superior place like Heaven. Anyway, Grandma disappeared the same way as she had appeared, leaving no trace except for cold air. That produced some sparks between Irka and myself. We argued about it but Irka still didn't know why ghosts usually left some cold air. I think it's because a dead person is pretty cold and that's bound to chill his soul. Irka decided not to tell anyone else about Grandma's visit. She reckoned Grandma just popped into the kitchen now because she didn't do so as a rule while she was alive. And furthermore, if Grandma wishes to visit anybody else in the house, no doubt she'll do so now that she's broken the ice.

3rd November 1939

AUNT Aniela started giving us lessons in literature, history and geography. This is to make sure that our brains don't get too rusty. I am glad we aren't to do maths. I hate it. I think the reason is that Aunt Aniela hates it too, though she didn't say so. She praised my reading and said that my compositions were quite good. I was very pleased to hear that because my last teacher had quite the reverse opinion. I was so encouraged by Aunt Aniela that I read the whole first volume of *By Fire and Sword* by Henryk Sienkiewicz. I enjoyed it very much but there was one word I did not understand, and when I asked what it meant, the boys started to giggle. Aunt Aniela's face turned pink and she said she'll explain it to me later as we couldn't waste the time during our lesson. The trouble with me is that I don't know what questions to ask and what questions not to ask. I wish there was some sort of way of finding out beforehand, that is before everyone gets embarrassed. So after lunch I went for a consultation with Papa. He said that grown-ups get embarrassed because either they don't know the answer themselves, in which case they ought to say so, or they don't know how to explain it to somebody else. Therefore, said Papa, there isn't an easy way of finding out except by improving one's standard of general education. I'll have to do just that. It would be so nice to know so much that you don't have to ask anything.

4th November 1939

GRANDPA is worried that Samson has tummy trouble. He said that Samson has been constipated for three days. Uncle Tadeusz wondered how Grandpa knew that Samson is constipated. Grandpa said that Samson's always been very regular, but alas it is no longer the case. Grandpa's been looking over the usual spots and found not a thing. He thinks that Samson needs loosening of his bowels. Uncle Tadeusz said it was nonsense. Horses don't get constipated, he said. And why not, Grandpa argued. Horses get tummy upsets just like human beings and in his opinion Samson needs a dose of laxative. Whether Uncle was too tired to argue, or whether he felt that Grandpa could be right, he suggested liquid paraffin as a remedy. But Grandpa didn't like that artificial stuff and brewed some senna pods for Samson. Poor Samson. I won't describe what happened except that it did work, and still is working. Now Grandpa is looking in our medicine chest for something to reverse the process.

5th November 1939

THE Gerries have declared that the city of Warsaw is to be called a Protectorate. Papa wants to know who is going to protect whom and against whom? The primary schools and the commercial colleges will be opened, but no higher education such as gymnasiums, lyceums and universities. They will remain closed. Papa said that a well-educated Polish population is against the interests of the Nazis. All they want of us is to labour for them. This is something that we all should try to resist. We can't refuse to work but we can work at a snail's pace, Papa said.

This afternoon we've been digging out carrots and storing them in dry sand. This is a nasty job and I could hardly wait till the last lot was brought in by Papa and Uncle Tadeusz. We put the carrots in layers in wooden boxes. Then Uncle covered them with sand, then another layer, and so on, ending up with a layer of sand. By the time we'd finished the job, I'd had enough of carrots to last me for a long time. But no. Mama had the bright idea of giving us some more carrots for supper. It would do us good, she said, plonking on the table a huge dish of stewed carrots with microscopic pieces of rabbit. Fortunately there was an apple charlotte to follow and it did soften the blow, for me at any rate. As I grumbled so much about the first course, Mama gave me two slices of cake to keep me quiet.

9th November 1939

NEITHER the rain nor the wind has been beating about the bush, at the start of their season. Uprooted trees and ripped roofs, flooded fields and muddy roads, are just a few things adding to our current gloom and doom. The Gerries are winning the war, and there's absolutely nothing cheerful to write about. I am just fed up.

11th November 1939

WE'VE been to church to pray for our heroes. So many young men have died and to no avail. Father Jakob read out the names of people from our parish. We prayed for the unknown soldiers at home and abroad. We prayed for our allies, the British, and their victory. When we got home, Grandpa lit a candle under the cross of Jesus Christ and he asked Irka to read to him from the Bible. Irka tried as well as she could but she gets short of breath. Her voice gets husky and she's often coughing. The damp air doesn't suit Irka's chest.

After lunch, Uncle Tadeusz and Tadek were digging out the dahlia tubers and Jurek and Wojtek were putting them into large flat baskets. Later on, in the evening, we packed them in sand the same way as carrots. Uncle Tadeusz said that the tubers dry out too much if they are left uncovered. If storing of carrots was a nasty job, storing of dahlias is even worse. Handling the muddy and cold tubers is like fondling dead frogs. When we emerged from the cold cellar, Mama gave us some hot milk with honey. It cheered us up no end. And then she said we were to have some sauerkraut with smoked sausage for supper. Papa was particularly pleased as it is his favourite meal.

12th November 1939

IT is getting very chilly. Aunt Stefa and Aunt Aniela have been putting in the double windows and filling in the spaces with cotton-wool. Over each joint, they glued a strip of white paper. We can feel the difference already though so far, only the windows have been insulated. Tomorrow, they'll tackle the french doors which is a big job. The oleander trees, growing in tubs, were brought indoors as was the big agava from the circular flower-bed. Uncle Tadeusz said that, any night now, we'll get a severe frost. And no doubt he's right because after a rainy spell in November it's time for the frost to wave its wand. And it usually does on the first night of the full moon. Its icy fingers grip the soil and its silver stare stills the water. Rivers and ponds petrify under its chilly gaze. From then on the frost holds sway until the spring looks in once more. I like the winter time. Saint Nicholas and Christmas and New Year's Eve, such a lot of reason for a truly festive season.

14th November 1939

PAPA held a secret meeting with four other men. I have never seen them before, but they were not strangers to Papa. They called him by his Christian name. I think they must be Papa's friends from Warsaw who are interested in politics because after they'd finished two rounds of vodka, they were listening to Papa's wireless or maybe they put a new set in the place of the old one. When they finished talking to Papa, they didn't go out through the front gate, but they went through a hole in the fence and disappeared into the fields and then nearby woodland. I wanted to ask Papa who they were, but one look at Papa's face told me it would have been no good. I expect they must be some sort of very secret agents.

16th November 1939

THE weather has turned quite cold. The big stove in the dining room has been lit for the first time this autumn. It stands in the corner of the room and is made of green tiles. It takes ages to warm up, but when it does the whole room is nearly as cosy as the kitchen. The stove reaches to the ceiling and it is filled with coal only once a day. Everyone likes to lean against the warm tiles. Uncle Tadeusz said that we hang on to it like leeches. His recipe for keeping warm is to get on with some work. Uncle Tadeusz never gets cold. His complexion is ruddy. He has short, greying hair, a small moustache under a prominent nose which he inherited from Grandma. He's rather stocky with a much bigger middle than Papa. When he bends down, he puts his legs wide apart, looking from the back not unlike the Arc de Triomphe. Uncle is very dependable, capable, plus all the other -ables and also very square. Auntie Stefa, who often argues with him, said once that she wouldn't be surprised if mother earth was not too round for Uncle Tadeusz. But I think she really likes him; after all, he's her only brother. I like my brother Wojtek and, in spite of his talent, he can be quite tiresome sometimes.

18th November 1939

GRANDPA said that we have mice in the cellar. They've been after our maize. So Grandpa borrowed Rasputin from his brother, Great-Uncle Emil. But I don't think the experiment has worked out the way Grandpa was hoping it would. Apparently, Rasputin was not overjoyed at being locked in our cold cellar. He miaowed all the time so I let him out, pretending to have forgotten to shut the door. I felt sorry for old Rasputin. I am sure he feels it's beneath his dignity to catch mice. Also he could be a vegetarian by conviction. I have never seen him eating meat, but he loves milk. Great-Uncle Emil said that once he caught Rasputin licking one of his cow's udders. It just shows what a clever cat he is in spite of, or perhaps because of, his name. I suppose it would be true to say that he's not a pretty cat. But his lack of looks is compensated for by his acquisition of wisdom. He's got plenty of that and he knows it. I wouldn't be surprised if he thought himself to be the cat's whiskers. Grandpa most certainly doesn't think him that. He said Rasputin was a useless animal not worthy of his keep. Since Rasputin is a milkoholic, Grandpa can't be right.

20th November 1939

GRANDPA set a mouse-trap in the cellar and he caught his finger in it. Now he has a nasty bruise. He also uttered a few words which he generally reserves for his brother, Emil. There's no doubt that the mice got under Grandpa's skin and he just had to vent his feelings. Papa suggested giving the mice a bit of goat's cheese. He was sure it would put them off from nibbling the maize. Mama gave Papa a dirty look just as Papa was about to enjoy his own joke. But Grandpa thought it was a good idea to poison the mice. He made a concoction which looked positively evil and, last night, he deposited it close to the sack of maize. This morning it was still there, untouched. Grandpa knows when he's beaten, so in the end he brought the sack upstairs and put it by his bed. Aunt Stefa said it was a silly thing to do as it might encourage the mice to share Grandpa's bedroom. We are just waiting to see if Grandpa will get his little visitors.

22nd November 1939

WE'VE been doing *Romeo and Juliet* with Aunt Aniela. She said that I was to read the part of Juliet and Jurek was to read the part of Romeo. Honestly, I can't think of anyone less like Romeo than our Jurek. Listening to Jurek's acting was like watching a buffalo dancing *Giselle*. After ten minutes even Aunt Aniela had had enough. We switched to geography. I enjoyed myself drawing maps. We had to mark towns, rivers, lakes, etc. on all the European countries. It was very interesting.

After lunch Irka wrapped Danúska in a warm blanket, put her in the pram and we went for a walk. Pempela decided to come as well. We went along the country path leading to the pond. In November, the picture of the countryside looks dismal. The usually blue sky changes to grey, the fields are khaki-brown and the trees remind one of upside-down brooms. There's not a chirrup, not a single bird-song, only the cawing of crows who flock into the fields to feed on grain. Irka said that she wants Danúska to be a secretary. She wants her to live in Warsaw with the gentlefolk, not in our village. Irka thinks Borowa-Góra to be dull and boring, but I don't think so. I prefer to walk in woods and meadows rather than along hard pavements with tall buildings on both sides of the street. In Warsaw, one can't see the sky and apart from a few trees everything is man-made. People have to look at and listen to people and be with other people all the time. There's nowhere to be alone. I don't dislike big cities, in fact I quite miss Warsaw just now, but on the whole I prefer the country where one can hear one's thoughts.

26th November 1939

THE Gerries have been deporting young men from our village to work on the farms in Germany. They need the labour. Mama is worried about the boys, but Uncle Tadeusz reckons they're still too young. Papa said that there is bad news from battles at sea. British and Polish liners have been sunk by German mines. Papa was so depressed that he went to bed early. Grandpa said that if the Gerries win the war it won't be worth living. If they win the war Poland will be lost forever, that's what Grandpa said, and it made me very sad.

28th November 1939

UNCLE Tadeusz was very pleased when he poked his head into the kitchen. We were as industrious as he likes us to be, making *golombki*. It was Mama's way to get our Papa out of his dumps. He's beside himself, in need of cheering up. I have never seen Papa so unhappy. Stuffed cabbage leaves is his favourite dish and Mama felt it might restore our Papa's mood. Our family, being fond of eating even more than talking, joined wholeheartedly in making the *golombki*. Irka chose the two largest cabbages she could find. She cut out the stems carefully and plunged the cabbages in boiling water while Mama prepared the stuffing. It consisted of minced meat, cooked rice, tomato purée and a chopped onion. After the cabbage leaves became sufficiently pliable, Irka separated each leaf and we started to make little parcels containing one tablespoon of the stuffing. Mama insisted that the parcels should be neat and tidy. Irka packed them into a large flat pan, poured in some hot water and covered the pan with the lid. She put it on top of our kitchen range and left it to simmer for two hours. When the *golombki* were tender, Mama made a delicious cheese and mustard sauce. Auntie Stefa laid the table and told Papa to hurry up but he said that he wasn't hungry. So Auntie poured him a tot of vodka and dear Papa was once again able to face the world. After a plateful of *golombki* Papa was himself again.

1st December 1939

DECEMBER is my favourite month for many reasons, and needless to say, Saint Nicholas' Day and Christmas Day are just two of them. Of course, our festivities won't be the same this year, but we are going to enjoy ourselves just the same. Papa and Uncle Tadeusz have been busy collecting lots of logs. Grandpa's managed to get a few bottles of home-made beer and some dried mushrooms in exchange for pickled gherkins. Also, the ex-gamekeeper from Radziwil's estate has promised us a couple of pheasants and a hare. Mama knows how to prepare pheasants and she can make hare pâté like no-one else. I've already started making my Christmas presents: hankies for the gentlemen and fudge sweetmeats for the ladies. Although Samson is not a lady, he has no use for a handkerchief but he has a sweet tooth, so he'll get a bag of fudge. Pempela is always a headache. I think a piece of her favourite sausage might be her idea of a treat. Danúska will get her blanket if I can get it finished by Christmas. If not, I'll give her a new feeder with a duck embroidered on it in yellow cotton. I am going to be ever so busy till Christmas, and probably will have to start getting up earlier than usual.

2nd December 1939

TODAY we had our first sprinkling of snow, but it didn't last. As soon as it touched the earth it melted away. I am sorry in a way, because I like the snow, but Grandpa said there's more on the way. He can usually feel it in his bones. I like snow for Christmas because mother earth looks so lovely and holy, all dressed up for little Jesus. Mama is making a new pleated skirt for me, in navy blue, and I have a pair of new ribbons in the same colour which I am saving for the big day. It's just three weeks away. Roll on, Christmas!

4th December 1939

IT'S Saint Barbara's Day today and it's been thawing, which means that Christmas will be frosty. I believe in this saying because it always comes out right. I think Wojtek's been painting pictures to give as presents. He locked his door but I could see through the key-hole what he's been up to. Jurek has been exceptionally good lately. He's afraid that Saint Nicholas won't give him a present if he carries on in his usual way. Every night he's even been brushing his teeth, without prompting from Aunt Stefa.

After dinner Aunt Aniela was showing us how to make Christmas decorations from coloured paper. I am making a chain from yellow, orange, red and pink colours and it will have to be several metres long to go around the Christmas tree at least three times. Wojtek has made some white parachutes with little angels suspended from them by cotton threads. They look awfully cute. Jurek's been painting clowns' faces on eggshells, then sticking hats on top of the shells and frilly collars around the other ends. Aunt Aniela said they were very funny clowns and suggested he might try to stick red noses on them as well. She's been making silver and gold stars. We've had a super time today.

6th December 1939

TODAY is Saint Nicholas' Day and our Grandpa's name-day, because his Christian name is Nicholas. When he was younger he used to dress up as Saint Nicholas in a red coat and hat. He would harness Samson to our sleigh and distribute presents to all the children in the village. As soon as they heard the sleigh-bells they would run to their gates calling, "Saint Nicholas is coming to see us!" I used to think it was a real Saint Nicholas from Heaven when I was younger. But Wojtek told me it wasn't the Saint but our Grandpa. Today it was Uncle Tadeusz who performed that long-standing custom. He came through the front door carrying a sack on his back, pretending it was terribly heavy. Mama and Aunt Stefa asked him whether he'd had a good journey and he said it was very cold up there in Heaven, and that he wouldn't mind a little drink if there was anything handy. Mama was going to give him some cocoa, but Saint Nicholas said that he would prefer something that is forbidden in Heaven. Papa knew at once what it was and poured him a glass of vodka. All the children from next door were trying to pierce the sack with their eyes, but Saint Nicholas wasn't in a hurry to give out the presents. He wanted to know whether we all worked hard helping our parents. I remember Grandpa used to ask us whether we all said our prayers regularly. After three glasses of vodka, Saint Nicholas at last felt in the mood to dive into the sack, but by then his sight had got somewhat fuddled and Mama had to help him to read the names on the packages. We thanked Saint Nicholas for remembering us and Jurek invited him to come the next year again. From the feel of the package I knew my gift from Saint Nicholas was a book. When I tore off the wrapping, I was amazed. It was a book all right, but in English. Aunt Aniela translated the title and it was called *Little Women*. She said we'll read it together. I was so pleased because it's my first book in English. It looks very difficult, but I shall have to finish reading it before the English soldiers arrive. After all the excitement and the few drops of vodka, Saint Nicholas had a job to walk straight. Aunt Aniela asked whether he might like to take a little nap before going back to his Heaven, and he said that was a good idea.

8th December 1939

I THINK our Tadek has a girlfriend. Her name is Janka. She's the shopkeeper's daughter and she wears high-heeled shoes. Why I think that Tadek is in love is because, every morning for the past week, Tadek has been fetching the bread. He goes shopping even when he has nothing to buy. When I asked him whether he was in love with Janka, he blushed and said that he was not. Then I asked him why he was blushing then. He said that I was exceedingly silly and infants like myself should stick to their dummies. I pointed out to him that the sheer fact that I've noticed it means that I am not an infant. And, furthermore, Janka knows that he's in love with her because I've told her. I didn't see why Tadek should be so coy about his feelings for Janka. After all, he is sixteen and he does wear long trousers.

11th December 1939

I'VE been helping Mama to make some walnut and honey fingers for Christmas. We got Wojtek to crack and shell the walnuts but he kept on nibbling them like a squirrel. Mama had to keep telling him that there wouldn't be enough left if he carried on putting one in the bowl and two into his stomach. When the nuts were shelled, Mama put one cup of honey and a large knob of butter into a saucepan and heated it gently until the mixture came to the boil. Then she added the nuts and mixed them in thoroughly. Meanwhile, I placed a wafer biscuit on the pastry board and Mama spread the nuts mixture all over it. Finally she pressed another wafer on top, and when the mixture was set she cut the wafer into dainty fingers. We ate a few broken bits and they tasted absolutely super.

14th December 1939

PAPA says that the French and the British will attack the Germans in the spring. We must wait and hope and keep our fingers crossed. Meanwhile the people in the villages are devising new ways of hiding food away from the Gerries. Apparently, their army is like a swarm of locusts, people say. Uncle Tadeusz made a hide-out at the back of our barn. The barn has been partitioned and the entrance to the food-store has been camouflaged with bundles of straw. This is just in case our cellar gets raided by the Gerries. The longer we live with our enemies, the more we learn about their disregard for human lives and rights. Papa said that in Warsaw there's a severe shortage of food. The Polish zloty can buy very little. The only way to do business is to exchange goods. In Warsaw the supply of coal is dwindling and consequently gas is a scarce commodity too. The electricity comes on in the streets used mainly by German troops. The Poles in Warsaw use oil lamps if they can get the paraffin, or carbide lamps which give quite a lot of light and are cheaper than candles.

In Warsaw the people are not allowed to walk about the streets after nine o'clock in the evening. Papa says that the people of Warsaw have an awful lot to put up with.

16th December 1939

WHEN I got up this morning and looked out, I was dazed by the glistening glory. Ten centimetres of snow fell during the night and it seemed so fluffy and as light as duck's down. After a hasty breakfast I went outside to marvel at, and to touch, the snow. To me it is the eighth wonder of the world. Only snow has the cosmetic skill to turn an ugly eyesore into an object of sheer beauty. It also purifies the air. The sun has already climbed above the tops of the pines, eager to take a look at the new scene. The same lime trees which a while ago shivered in their trunks were standing so still, as if fearful of losing their newly acquired apparel. Every branch and every twig has been sprinkled with white. What a delight. I was reluctant to walk over this endless perfection. Almost afraid to spoil the vision of my sight's resurrection. There were tints of blue in the shade and the glow of pink where the sun stroked the snow. I stood amidst the wonderland hypnotised by its beauty, until Mama broke the spell. She said I'd catch my death without my winter coat.

18th December 1939

ALTHOUGH Tadek loves Janka, I am not at all sure that Janka loves Tadek. When I took a twig of fir tree for Janka to kiss, she said it was too prickly. I said it was for Tadek to keep by his bed, but she still wouldn't do it. In my view that's not love. I suppose it's not my business, but I should like to know why Janka doesn't fancy our Tadek. Of course, she could be too pretty for our Tadek. Janka has blonde hair and hazel eyes. Whereas Tadek is very ordinary. I wouldn't call him handsome. Though

94

he's better looking than Jurek. After lunch, Tadek, Wojtek, Jurek and myself went into the hills where the slopes are just right for skiing. Janka came with us and she brought her sleigh. It is over a metre long and four people can sit on it. By the time we'd climbed the highest hill I was nearly out of breath. Jurek went down the hill first, partly on his skis but mostly on his bottom. He looked none the worse for it. When he'd climbed up again he was determined to show us that he can really ski. But by then the four of us, huddled on Janka's sleigh, were hurtling down the slope at terrific speed. It was the most exhilarating experience I can remember. When the sun was almost touching the distant fields we started for home. We were exhausted and were puffing clouds of air like steam engines. Janka and Tadek were playing snowballs. I think she really likes Tadek, only pretends she doesn't.

19th December 1939

I AM so stiff today that I can hardly move. Mama said it serves me right. Mama can be unfeeling at times. She could show me some sympathy at least. The frost has eased and there is a thaw on the way. Wojtek's made a snowman which looks very much like Hitler. He made the moustache from an old broom, the eyes from a broken beer bottle and he put a swastika on his left arm. His right arm was raised in the Nazi salute. On his head, he had Grandma's old chamber-pot. We all laughed so much. Our Wojtek is really quite clever. Uncle Tadeusz, however, told Wojtek to demolish it. He said it was too much like the Führer and it was too dangerous. He reminded us what happened to little Gabriel. So we armed ourselves with sticks and bottles and had a go at Hitler with unbelievable pleasure. First went his arm, then his head hurtled off. His rounded belly was speared with a broomstick, and finally he collapsed, reduced to a mere heap of snow. Wojtek stuck a little white and red flag on top of the rubble signifying our victory. The three of us stood to attention and sang the Polish national anthem.

20th December 1939

MAMA, Aunt Stefa and Irka have been very busy in the kitchen preparing food for Christmas. Irka, bent over the grater, was making horse-radish and beetroot pickle. It is nice to eat with cold meats but it is tiresome to make. The horse-radish is worse than onions. Irka's cheeks were streaming with tears. Aunt Stefa said it was good for one's eyes but she doesn't like this job herself. By the time poor Irka had grated two sticks, Mama had to take over. The cooked beetroots are easy to grate. When Mama had a sufficient quantity of both, she mixed them together, added some cream and packed the mixture into glass jars, and well sealed the tops. Mama said it should keep in a cold cellar for several weeks. They also marinated some raw fillets of herrings in white vinegar spiced with slices of onions and whole peppercorns. This is one of the traditional dishes served on Christmas Eve.

21st December 1939

PAPA said that our family has been neglecting the goat. The poor Nanny has been the Cinderella. She hasn't got a name even. Papa is quite right. The goat has been so generous with her milk and we've been so mean with our affections. So we've christened her Cindy. Irka, who generally milks her every day, said that she has a lovely disposition. There's only one thing Cindy doesn't like and that is cold hands. Irka has to warm her hands in warm water before she touches Cindy's milk-taps. I'll have to think of a suitable present for our Cindy. Perhaps a glass slipper might be an idea. But I expect she would prefer a billy-goat to be her Prince Charming.

22nd December 1939

TADEK, Wojtek, Jurek and I went to the woods today to find a Christmas tree. When we got about half-way the snow was so deep that I had a job to keep up with the boys. Wojtek said I could sit on the sleigh while they pulled me. The path to the woods was completely snowbound. There were drifts in places half a metre high. When we actually got among the trees the snow was quite shallow. I was surprised to see so many different animals' footprints. Although the woodland looks deserted, obviously it is the animals' kingdom sheltering under the umbrellas of pine trees. With the snow piled on top like a meringue, it felt warm beneath this natural roof. We walked slowly, inspecting every fir tree and at last came across one which looked symmetrical. Tadek said it wasn't tall enough, but in the end we decided to cut this one. He said it wouldn't reach the ceiling in the dining room. Every year we have had a big Christmas tree, but this year it will have to be a smaller one. Tadek and Wojtek cut the tree, tied it with some string to the sleigh, and we started on our way back. As we reached a clearing the snow was deeper there. Jurek started to throw snowballs at me, so I thought I would show him. As I bent down to pick up some snow, I noticed a black boot sticking out from a snowdrift. I called Tadek. Tadek kicked the boot and then we saw part of a human leg clad in the black boot and we recognised a German uniform. The rest of the corpse was covered by snow. I was terrified. Tadek told the boys not to touch it. He said the best thing was to cover the leg which was sticking out with snow and get home quickly. Wojtek said that we should try to camouflage our footprints. But that was easier said than done. Tadek said that we should not hang around, otherwise the Gerries might think we'd killed that soldier. We hurried home as fast as we could. When we arrived back, I was utterly exhausted. My underclothes were sticking to my sweating body. Papa and Uncle Tadeusz were very concerned when they heard about our discovery in the woods. When night fell, Papa and Uncle took their spades and went to bury the corpse. I was petrified in case something should happen to Papa and Uncle.

23rd December 1939

AT breakfast time Papa said to us that we should try to forget the dead soldier in the woods and mustn't talk to anyone about it. Of course we wouldn't, but I should like to know who killed him just the same. I gathered from Irka that he wasn't a casualty from the battle-field. She thinks it could be something to do with Papa's friends who came to visit him the other day. I hope she's wrong. I should hate my Papa to be connected in any way with that dead soldier. I couldn't sleep last night. And when I dropped off, I was having nightmares. I dreamt that I was trying to run through deep snow and I was falling over the dead soldier's boot. I dreamt the same dream three times last night, and on each occasion I woke up covered in sweat.

This afternoon, Mama and Aunt Stefa were baking bread and cakes for Christmas in the old bakery. The smell was gorgeous. Everybody was sniffing and drooling as they passed the bakery. Mama made two sultana cakes, one apple and cinnamon slice, and a carrot and prune flan. The scent of vanilla and other spices wafted right across the courtyard. Lovely. Irka and Aunt Aniela were busy in the kitchen cooking *bigos*. This is a traditional Christmas dish which everybody likes, and Papa adores it. It is made from sauerkraut, with different kinds of meat including garlic sausage, plus carrots and onions. It is stewed for hours and reheated when needed. The longer it stands, the better it gets. Irka made a large quantity of *bigos* knowing how popular it is among our family, though the smell of cooking sauerkraut is far from pleasant. When it was cooked, Irka put the covered saucepan on the balcony to freeze. She simply chops out lumps of it when required.

24th December 1939

CHRISTMAS Eve is here at last. The last few days have been hectic. I have wrapped and labelled all my presents and Aunt Aniela put them under the Christmas tree for me. The children are not allowed to go into the dining room because Aunt Aniela and Papa are dressing the tree. This morning we had our baths and Grandpa washed his feet and put on a pair of clean socks. Uncle Tadeusz made new straw beds for Samson and Cindy, and I brushed Pempela's coat and told her not to get dirty. Everybody, except little Danúska, has been fasting today till the Eve supper, which is the climax of our festivities. Although we eat a meatless supper, the whole affair is far from modest. When the Bethlehem star appears in the sky it is time to break the rice wafer. Grandpa takes the plate with the *oplatek* and says, "Blessings to our Lord Jesus and to you all, my children." Everybody takes a bit of *oplatek* and we all kiss and hug and wish each other a happy Christmas. Then we enter the dining room and set our eyes for the first time on the Christmas tree. With oohs and ahs everyone admires the splendid decorations, and I usually take a little peep at what's underneath the Christmas tree. From the mountains of presents I can sometimes spot one with my name on it. Everybody looks very smart and the ladies have fresh hair-dos. This year our table has been laid with a white cloth and the best china, and decorated with tiny fir twigs. Grandpa sat down first and we followed suit. The first course consisted of clear piping-hot red *barszcz* with a spoonful of sour cream in it. For the second course we had mushroom fritters fried in butter. After that came the main course of carp baked in cream with mushrooms. Mama served it with her special French rolls. The fish was very good but I liked the rolls even better. The sweet was best of all. It was a morello cherry flan with cream and brandy sauce. As usual Mama received full marks for a delicious meal. After the table had been cleared, Irka brought in a Russian samovar and put it in the middle of the table. Irka was wearing her red dress and she looked pretty in it.

And then something wonderful happened. Grandpa took little Danúska from her cot and very gently cradled her in his arms, saying, "Come to Grandpa, my little baby." We were very moved by Grandpa's gesture because, up to now, he had never taken much notice of Danúska, pretending she wasn't there. I could see Irka's face glowing with pleasure. Then the candles on the Christmas tree were lit and the whole atmosphere in the room had changed, like in a fairy-tale. Aunt Aniela intoned a carol *God is Born* and we all joined in. The samovar took over and started to sing, gently proclaiming that the tea was nearly ready. Uncle Tadeusz loves his tea the Russian way, with raspberry conserve. Jurek and Wojtek distributed the presents and I had many, many things, but Papa's present from Uncle Tadeusz was funniest of all. He had a bottle of vodka with a dummy stuck over the cork. Papa said it was just what he needs in bed when he gets a bit peckish. We sang and talked and joked until eleven o'clock and then it was time for the midnight mass. Grandpa went to harness Samson who was asleep and not very keen to come out into the cold. I gave him his fudge sweetmeats and it was only by wishing him a very happy Christmas that he agreed to co-operate. Samson likes the sleigh because it is easier to pull. Not everybody came to church. For one thing, there wasn't enough room in the sleigh, and for another only Grandpa, Mama, Irka and I were keen to come. The ride in a sleigh on a moonlit night is something one has to experience in order to appreciate its enchantment. Grandpa's sleigh is small but we managed to squeeze in, tucking woollen rugs around our legs. Samson wasn't very enthusiastic at first, but soon he perked up and joined in the fun. When we got into the open, the snow looked like shimmering water. Its glazed surface reflected the moonlight and the countryside assumed a wonderland quality, mysterious and elusive. From the main road we turned into the poplar lane and we were nearly there. We could hear the bells calling the faithful for the midnight mass. The people were arriving from all directions all dressed in bulky coats and fur hats. We wiped the snow from our boots and entered the church which was already packed. There were fir branches stuck behind pictures and holy statues giving off a scent of resin. The candles were lit and then the choristers came, followed by Father Jakob, and the mass had begun. My eyes kept on straying to the manger where little Jesus lay upon the straw and Saint Mary and Joseph were kneeling beside Him.

25th December 1939

WE slept late today and so lunch was our breakfast. We had cold pork belly, hare pâté, dry garlic sausage and lots of different pickles such as gherkins, horse-radish and beetroot pickle, pears, red plums and sauerkraut salad. Mama served home-baked rye bread which is greatly liked by our family. After lunch we played games. Uncle Tadeusz hid various objects all over the room and we had to look for them. The one who completed that task first won the prize which was a bag of sweets for children and a bottle of mead for grown-ups. After tea the carol singers arrived, holding a gold star with a lighted candle in the centre. They were two brothers, Jacek and Tomek, and two younger boys from the next village. They sang carols and read the nativity story from the Bible. Mama made some hot beer with sugar and yolks and invited them for a drink and a piece of sultana cake. Papa gave them two zloty and they wanted to sing more carols but Uncle Tadeusz said that if they went to sing next door they might get more zloty. I was sorry they didn't stay a bit longer but Uncle was not.

26th December 1939

GRANDPA took Irka and Danúska in his sleigh so that they could spend a day with Irka's step-mother. The house seemed empty without them. But our peaceful Christmas came to an abrupt end when three soldiers arrived, creating a heck of a commotion. I gathered from the rumpus that they were looking for their missing comrade. They looked all over the house, the outbuildings, the greenhouse, the privy and the shrubbery in the garden. Papa and Uncle Tadeusz looked pale but calm. I was very scared. After half-an-hour they were gone and with them went the spirit of Christmas. It was a brutal reminder that our country is occupied and the bloody war is going on, though we can't actually hear the guns. I heard Papa talking to Uncle Tadeusz. Papa said that the Gerries' dogs might sniff out the grave, and the footprints in the snow will lead them back to the house. Uncle doubted whether they would because the grave was deep, and we've had a snowfall since then. Papa pointed out that there wasn't enough snow, and if only those stupid friends of his hadn't acted in such haste. Uncle said it was no good blaming them when there's no clear indication as to who did it, and the best thing is to forget it. This is something I can't do. I am constantly uneasy and it's always preying on my mind. I hate that dead soldier because he's ruined everything. I know it's wrong to hate a dead man, but I wouldn't hate him if we hadn't found his body in that snow-drift. When I said my prayers, I asked God for more snow.

28th December 1939

WHETHER it was in answer to my prayer, or perhaps Papa's and Uncle's, the heavens opened and the snow came tumbling down. This morning we had a job to open the front door. Like badgers, we've been burrowing through at least a metre of snow. Everyone has been digging and shovelling until the courtyard resembled a badger's set. In spite of huffing and puffing, Papa and Uncle Tadeusz were in good spirits, which they further fortified with a drop of vodka. Although we were isolated by this sudden snowfall, we also felt insulated from the Gerries. They can't do much against nature any more than we can. Mama and Aunt Stefa took advantage of easy water and filled all the available buckets and bowls with snow. Melted snow makes lovely soft water for washing.

1st January 1940

TODAY is the first day of January, nineteen-forty. Last year seemed as long as two years put together. So much happened in nineteen-thirty-nine that no doubt it will go down in history as the year of disasters. Papa thinks that nineteen-forty will be a better year, working on the assumption that it could hardly be a worse one. This is what he said when he proposed a toast last night on the stroke of midnight. Father Jakob came to greet the New Year with us and we enjoyed his company very much. Mama insisted that everyone, including Grandpa and Pempela, should have a good wash today. Mama says that if one doesn't take the trouble to wash on the first of January, one will remain dirty throughout the rest of the year. That's probably why Grandpa has been dodging Mama ever since he got up. Very likely he too wished to save his skin from abuse and save the water from misuse during the current year. But Mama can be determined when she wants to be. And this morning she proved it. Having made sure that the rest of the family were clean and tidy, Mama set off to look for Grandpa. "Tata", she shrilled at the top of her voice, but he was nowhere to be seen and nowhere to be heard. It isn't easy to get lost on our smallholding without a determined effort. Mama knows that as well as Grandpa. So she went methodically through the obvious places like the privy, the stable, the bakery, and so on, but there was no sign of Grandpa. My bet is that Grandpa remembers last New Year's Day and wasn't having any nonsense this year. "Have you seen Grandpa?" Mama asked everybody she came across. She was getting a little flushed but more determined than ever that Grandpa also should have his bath. When she approached the boys, Wojtek and Jurek fled like flies, but she caught them in the nick of time. She told them to go and look for Grandpa and warned them not to come back till they had found him. By now, lunch time was approaching and no doubt Grandpa felt that, if he could stay away till then, Mama would get fed up. But she didn't. She pushed the tin bath under the kitchen table and got on with the finishing touches to our special meal. The aroma of Mama's cuisine brought Grandpa out from his hideout. He settled himself in his favourite armchair with his rosary, uttering a thankful prayer, when Mama seized him. There were no buts about it. Poor Grandpa had his nasty bath while everybody else was enjoying the delights of roasted pheasant. When I went to fill Pempela's bowl, I could hear Grandpa grumbling aloud. He was telling God about the folly of having children who later in life turn against their own father.

3rd January 1940

SEVERE frost has gripped Poland as far south as Kraków. Last night we had minus twenty Celsius. The water in the well is solid and we have to use snow for cooking. Water from snow is good for washing but not so good for tea. I could taste the snow in my glass of tea, so could Papa. He disguised his with a drop of rum. After too generous a topping-up with rum, Mama wanted to know whether Papa could still taste the tea. Papa answered that the purpose of adding rum was so that he shouldn't taste tea at all. Mama asked why then bother to drink tea at all.

Papa replied that it was no bother to him. He, as a rule, always consumed what Mama put in front of him. Mama said she should hope so and he needn't be so pious about it. The argument went on longer than usual until Grandpa told them to shut up "for pity's sake". They did just that. In blessed silence, we huddled around the stove for a read, or a little nap, according to one's preference.

5th January 1940

THE pond is frozen to a depth of thirty centimetres, so Mama had no qualms about us going skating. I am not as good at skating as Tadek or Wojtek, but nearly equal with Jurek. He says he's much better than me and he's been showing off doing a figure eight, but it looked more like a nought to me. Skating is my favourite winter sport, though I often end up with a sore bottom and several bruises. In spite of that it's worth it. When the surface of the ice is smooth, I can skate ever so fast and it's like gliding in air. Sometimes we play hockey with sticks and lumps of ice, but today we were practising jumping over heaps of snow. After my first jump I landed on my bottom and it wasn't a joke, though my dear cousins were laughing their heads off at my misfortune. Jurek shouted that I should tie a cushion to my seat. I felt like hitting him. Later on, other children from the village joined us, including Janka. Tadek and Janka were trying to dance but without much success. Probably because there wasn't any music, or, to be more accurate, because they were not very good at it. Janka was wearing a pair of navy-blue slacks, a white jumper, a red woolly hat with a pom-pom, and a scarf to match. She looked a stunner. Tadek thought so, too. He took her hand and they skated together round and round. I got quite dizzy just watching them. Later, he put his arm around her middle and she did likewise. They looked like Siamese twins and they didn't care two hoots what the others thought. So I thought I would let them know that I know about their romance. I skated right in front of them and said, "Isn't love grand?" They just ignored me, so I left them to their lovey-doveying, and tried to teach Pempela how to skate. I wish someone would design snow boots for our Pempela. Her pads must get terribly cold in winter.

6th January 1940

WE'VE been celebrating the festival of the Three Kings with the leftovers, which Mama transformed into a most scrumptious meal. It was also the last day of the Christmas tree. I am always sorry to see it being dismantled. Like all good things, the Christmas festivities have come to an end and Easter is a long way off.

In the afternoon, Grandpa took Mama, Aunt Stefa and Aunt Aniela for a ride in his sleigh. The small country road is covered with packed snow and its surface is almost like ice. So I put on my skates and had an enjoyable ride, holding on to the sleigh. Samson felt frisky today and trotted along merrily, neighing as if he were in his teens. When we got to the next village of Majdany, Grandpa decided to look up a friend of his, Miss Kolupa, who is now in her eighties and lives alone in an old wooden house thatched with straw. There is a huge stork's nest perched on the roof near the chimney stack. A few years back, a pair of storks used to nest there every spring. But they have never delivered any babies to Miss Kolupa. People call her the white witch. I could see why when we entered her home. She herself, and everything surrounding her, were quite extraordinary. Each wall was almost covered by pictures and photographs with hardly a space between them. The room was packed with furniture and junk of all sorts. The windows were curtained with dark net so that only a minimum of light filtered in. There was an open fire in the corner of the room and large logs were smouldering on it. A sooty kettle hung from a sooty chain. Miss Kolupa was sitting by the fire when we went in. It took her a few seconds to recognise Grandpa and when she did she was astonished that he should have aged so much. To me, she herself looked like an archaeological relic. Her face was a multitude of wrinkles, with tiny black eyes sunken in the folds of loose skin. She had only one tooth in her upper jaw and when she smiled it had a hypnotic quality. That solitary tooth drew one's sight to it the way a magnet attracts metal objects. It was difficult to imagine that this woman was young once upon a time. Grandpa exchanged a few words with her and wished her a happy New Year, giving her a little hamper which Mama had packed before we left the house. When we were on the way home I was persuaded to ride in the sleigh, and a good job too, for my legs felt jolly tired. I couldn't stop thinking of Miss Kolupa and how cruel the passing years can be to one's looks. Will I be looking like her when I am old? It doesn't bear thinking about.

9th January 1940

PAPA reported this morning that the Finns were fighting the Russians with great success. They destroyed a whole Russian division in a victorious battle near Lake Kianta. On the Western Front our allies are struggling against the Gerries. It was good to have some news again after the break when something was wrong with Papa's wireless.

After a rest over Christmas we resumed our lessons with Aunt Aniela. She's a good teacher and our lessons are varied and interesting. Aunt Aniela always discusses the difficult points in literature and she encourages us to comment and to criticise our essays. This is something we never did at school and I think it's a good idea.

Uncle Tadeusz is worried about the continuous severe frost and what it might do to his cherry orchard. Cherry trees can't stand prolonged frosty weather, Uncle Tadeusz said.

12th January 1940

TADEK'S been shaving his beard. Uncle Tadeusz laughed at him and wanted to know whether he had anything to shave. But Tadek insisted he had seven whiskers on his chin and was determined to have them off with Grandpa's razor. I know why Tadek wanted to have his whiskers off. It's because they tickled Janka. I saw him kissing her under the mistletoe. But the fact is, it wasn't mistletoe at all. It was a twig from a gorse bush and Janka didn't mind one little bit. They didn't know that I was watching them. Tadek came close to Janka, held out the prickly piece of gorse over her head and said, "Merry Christmas," even though it was already nearly the middle of January. Janka's face turned pink, and then shocking pink, as Tadek kissed her right on her lips. She didn't protest in the least. I think she enjoyed it. Then Tadek whispered something into her ear, and his face turned pink too, only it was more of a beetrooty colour. This manifestation of love took place just behind the bakery and I was on the other side, well screened from their view. I coughed twice before I emerged and said to them, "Good morning." They looked at me as if I had said something in Chinese and walked off together towards the pond. Well, if that's what love does to one's manners then it's hard luck on those who aren't in love.

19th January 1940

AUNT Aniela wants to go back to Warsaw. She's hoping the river Bug will freeze solid before long, then it should be relatively easy to cross the border to the Protectorate. Uncle Tadeusz said that life in Warsaw was much harder than it is here in Borowa-Góra, but Aunt Aniela was adamant. She even demonstrated to Uncle how miserable she was by shedding a few tears. Uncle said that he'll see what he can do but he couldn't promise for sure. There were too many problems which were beyond his powers. He also said that it was better for Aunt Aniela, in her present condition, to be where there was a reasonable amount of food. He said that she ought to think of the little stranger instead of herself. I don't agree with Uncle Tadeusz. I don't see why she should think of strangers when she's got herself and Uncle to think about. I think the war is getting on everybody's nerves. Even Pempela hasn't been herself lately. She's been biting her own tail. I told her it was a silly, futile thing to do. If she is vexed over something or other, she ought to have a good old barking spree and not just bite her tail. Aunt Stefa used to bite her nails when she had them. And that got her nowhere. It became a nasty habit and Grandpa had to paint her nails with something bitter. I wonder whether I should do the same to Pempela. She might bite her tail right off one of these days. Irka thinks it could be fleas. I can't imagine our Pempela having fleas. She moves only in the best circles. Though she has been gallivanting with that yapping fox-terrier who is her best friend. Well, I suppose, if one couldn't share one's troubles with a best friend, then life wouldn't be worth living.

22nd January 1940

THE small heated greenhouse is a lovely place to sit in. Though the chances of doing nothing in there are slim because it's Uncle's domain. The greenhouse is usually like a beehive with Uncle being the queen bee. Anyone who puts his foot in it has had it, because Uncle immediately grabs people to help with the work. Today was a sunny day, and the interior of the hot-house was looking like a green oasis amidst a snowy desert. Most tempting. So I went in. Uncle Tadeusz was pricking out little seedlings, and before I even closed the door he said that I was just the lady. He needed all the nimble fingers he could lay his hands on. So I was shown where to sit and what to do. Pricking out minute seedlings needs not only good eyesight and patience, but also a great deal of devotion. I wanted to know why Uncle talked to his plants. He said it was because they were his friends. I reminded him that he also ate them. Uncle Tadeusz explained that he talks to them when they are little and eats them when they get bigger. No wonder they don't answer him back. I am jolly glad I'm not a plant. Anyway, I don't think I love plants the way Uncle does. I pricked out two boxes of tomatoes and Uncle offered me a third box but I said I couldn't do any more. Instead of being grateful for the two I'd done, he was displeased about the third one which I didn't do. Sometimes I feel that grown-ups have no sense of fair play at all. Or is the law of justice always in their favour?

25th January 1940

IRKA is in bed again. She has a temperature and I've been looking after Danúska. I think she thinks I am her second Mama. It makes me feel very nice inside. By now I can feed Danúska, I can change her nappy and, lately, I've been bathing her entirely on my own. She is much more fun than a doll and she gurgles when I talk to her. Irka said she would miss me if we went back to Warsaw. Papa doesn't think we shall be going back just yet, though for schooling purposes it's better there. Aunt Aniela and Uncle Tadeusz are thinking of returning, if they can, when the weather gets better. Uncle feels that early summer should be soon enough, but Aunt Aniela is getting fed up here. She's missing her mother and her friends and the general atmosphere of a city. She loves the cinema, theatre and concerts, and she hates the privy. I suppose our life in Borowa-Góra is not a pinnacle of culture, but it is interesting to me.

28th January 1940

WOJTEK had a nasty accident today. He went skating with Tadek and Jurek and they were racing. Wojtek fell flat on his face and broke his front tooth. It just snapped in half. He brought the broken tooth to show it to Mama. She nearly fainted when she saw the ugly gap. Apart from his teeth, Wojtek seemed all right. He had a sore knee and a scratch on one side of his face. Mama was far more upset over his tooth than Wojtek was. He wanted to go back skating but Mama put her foot down. She told him off for playing dangerous games. Fortunately, the remaining half of the tooth appears to be still firmly anchored to his jaw and wasn't as painful as one would expect. Papa told Wojtek to sit quietly and get on with some painting. Aunt Aniela suggested that Wojtek might try to paint Miss Kolupa. In her opinion she's a most interesting subject, a painter's dream, as she put it. When Aunt Aniela had finished describing to Wojtek Miss Kolupa's features, Wojtek became fascinated by her looks and said he'll ask her to sit for him. Papa said if he painted her in oils, perhaps her portrait would win him a place in the Warsaw Art Gallery. We all have high hopes that our Wojtek will be famous one day.

2nd February 1940

NOW we have a little pig keeping our Cindy company. Uncle Tadeusz exchanged some dry peas and beans for a little piglet. Aunt Stefa immediately plunged him into a bowl and scrubbed him with Grandpa's loofah. Grandpa had no objection to his toilet things being used for a pig. What he disapproved of was the indignation inflicted on that wretched animal. It was

111

against a pig's nature to be clean, and Grandpa, for one, whole-heartedly condemned Auntie's action. Rights or wrongs apart, the soapy water transformed the little piggy into a cuddly pink pet. He quite enjoyed being made a fuss of and didn't like going back to the smelly stables. He's been nicknamed "Porky". The pleasing think about Porky's face is that it has a cheerful expression. His mouth looks like a French croissant. People just have to smile back when they look at Porky's grin. I should say our little Porky is a clever pig. If he carries on charming us the way he did today, my guess is that no-one would have the heart to turn him into sausages. Oh dear, I've just remembered Uncle Tadeusz and his little seedlings.

4th February 1940

THE frost is still pursuing its vendetta against the Gerries, we hope. But it affects us too. Uncle Tadeusz has been trying to protect a number of young trees. He tied some straw around the stems of the standard roses and other plants. Whether this will stop them from freezing to death, Uncle is not at all sure. We've been getting through our stock of coal faster than expected. Frost is a dirty word in our house and Grandpa's been praying for a thaw. Papa, Uncle Tadeusz, Auntie Stefa and Aunt Aniela have started playing bridge in the evenings, which means arguments and quarrels. I wish they would play something more civilised, such as rummy. I hate it when they are shouting and neither Grandpa nor Pempela can stand the noise. I've been spending a lot of time with Irka in the kitchen and we discussed all sorts of subjects. She told me that Aunt Aniela is expecting a baby. She explained to me all about babies and it does make sense, because I've often wondered where the storks got the babies from. We are hoping that Aunt Aniela's baby will be a girl, of course. If it's a boy it could turn out to be like Uncle Tadeusz, and that wouldn't please her, I'm sure. Though Irka said that sometimes miracles happened where least expected. I hope she's right. In any case I'll keep my fingers crossed for a girl or a miracle, I don't mind which, so long as it isn't a replica of Uncle Tadeusz. Then we discussed the advantages and disadvantages of having husbands. She feels it's nice to have a husband if he's good, and nasty if he turns out to be horrid. I asked her whether there was any way of telling beforehand, that is before one gets married, what the future husband is going to be like. She said it was very difficult indeed because all men are nice at first. I reminded her about our Jurek. If there was an exception to the rule, surely Jurek was it. She said that Jurek is not a man just yet and that he might get better when he grows up. I personally doubt it, but I could be wrong. Then I asked her when a boy starts being a man, and she said when he starts to shave. I always thought it was when he put on a pair of long trousers. Now I understand why our Tadek was so keen to have his whiskers off. He wanted to be a man. Irka also explained to me about boys' voices changing, going through a squeaky stage, like Wojtek's. I didn't know our Wojtek was going to be a man. Well, not just yet. I wonder what Mama will do when she's got two men in the family, though Papa is getting on a bit, but I don't think he knows it. Irka said it was much easier to tell when a girl becomes a woman because her bosom begins to stick out. I inspected mine in the mirror and it doesn't stick out, thank goodness. I should hate to be a woman and say goodbye to all the fun and games. But Irka comforted me, saying that grown-ups also have fun and games, but of a different kind. What kind, I wanted to know, but she said I shall have to wait and see. I only hope they are good games, worth waiting for.

6th February 1940

I WENT to speak with Wojtek to see how much squeak he had in his voice. I asked him to talk to me but he said, about what? Anything, I said. He looked at me as if I was daft. All I wanted

113

him to do was to carry on talking for a minute or two, just long enough for me to find out whether he was turning into a man. But he wouldn't. He told me to buzz off. I only hope Wojtek's manners will improve before he becomes a husband.

When Janka came to ask how much bread we needed for tomorrow, I knew it was really to see Tadek. But Tadek wasn't in the house and she didn't want to ask where he was. Janka's bosom is sticking out and pointedly so. Which means that she's a woman, and I expect they'll get married. Though I doubt if Tadek would make an ideal husband. I rather think not, but definitely better than Jurek, or Wojtek for that matter. I asked Janka whether she wanted to know where Tadek was and she said not particularly, but if I were itching to tell her then she said I could go ahead. I said I was not itching to tell her anything. I thought that she was itching to know, that's all. She would have liked to scratch my eyes out if she could. Miaow!

9th February 1940

WE had cheese dumplings for dinner and they were a success. If only Papa and Uncle Tadeusz knew what kind of cheese Mama had used, but they didn't. As Mama said, what the brain doesn't know about, the mouth usually enjoys. And how right she was. I helped Mama with the dumplings, which are nearly as easy to make as they are to eat. Mama put two large boiled potatoes in the bowl and I mashed them. Then she added three cups of self-raising flour, one egg, and some cottage cheese. Our dear Cindy had provided the milk, and our dear Mama had made the cheese, ignoring people's unkind remarks. Mama kneaded the dough, then rolled it into a long sausage and cut it into two-centimetre-thick slices. We boiled the *kluski* in salted water, and when they swam up to the top, Mama fished them out. She piled the *kluski* onto a large plate, poured some melted butter over them and sprinkled more cheese on top. Papa munched through his dumpling and said it was quite tasty. Uncle Tadeusz wanted to know what he was eating. Mama answered short and sharp, "Your dinner."

11th February 1940

I WAS watching Wojtek talking to Papa and suddenly a high-pitched sound hit me on the ear. Undoubtedly that was a squeak. Yes, Wojtek's voice is definitely breaking. I wondered whether Papa had noticed. If he had, he said nothing. So I whispered to Papa that our Wojtek is going to be a man, and all Papa had to say was that he hoped so. He just carried on talking about Wojtek's painting, in which Papa takes particular interest. Miss Kolupa looks more of a witch in Wojtek's portrait than she does in real life. The wrinkles on her face are like the Norwegian fiords, and her eyes almost glow like black fire. In them there's a hint of sadness mixed with a smile. Her curved lips reveal a horn-like tooth. A black or a white witch? I wonder which witch Wojtek's eyes saw? That's what I want to know. Papa said that the portrait was good, and he suggested to Wojtek that he shouldn't hurry. He wants him to take time over it. I agree with Papa because Wojtek always wants to finish everything at once. I wish I could paint as well as he does. I tried once, but after Mama asked me what it was supposed to be I became convinced that my efforts would never stir the human soul.

13th February 1940

GRANDPA was grumpy today. He has tummy trouble and he made no bones about it. Ever since he got up he's been going to and fro between the kitchen and the privy. He wanted Mama to brew him some senna-pods. Mama said that he needed the opposite. Grandpa insisted that he must have something to get

115

rid of the bugs, but Mama offered him some fuller's earth sprinkled with sugar. Grandpa took a mouthful of Mama's paste and his face turned the same colour. I really thought poor Grandpa was going to cry. Instead, he slung the paste into the dustbin, together with the plate. Mama yelped, not unlike an injured Pempela, and dived to retrieve her best china. She pulled out two halves, held together by the sticky paste. When she was just about to explode, Father Jakob popped his head round the door with a "Coo-ee". He was beaming all over and wanted to know how his "dear children" were today. I could tell from Mama's face that she'd much rather see Father Jakob at his altar than in her kitchen at that precise moment. No doubt Grandpa thought that God had taken his side and sent him a saviour. He sneaked out, leaving Mama and Father Jakob to have a lovely little chat.

15th February 1940

AUNT Stefa bandaged Pempela in a towel sprinkled with paraffin. At last her fleas were in for the high jump. Judging by Pempela's whimpering, the question was who hated the paraffin more, the fleas or the dog? When Auntie took the towel off, the horrid pests popped out from between Pempela's fur, seeking sanctuary on Auntie's legs. I should have kept quiet. Being impulsive, as I undoubtedly am, I pointed out to Auntie where all the fleas had gone. Aunt Stefa appeared to have had even less restraint than I. She started bouncing up and down, throwing off her skirt, stockings, and even her drawers. Then she grabbed Pempela's towel and wrapped it around her middle. I knew that if I hung around a minute longer the fleas wouldn't. The best thing was to call Mama. So I ran as fast as I could, yelling for help. Mama rushed in with a stick. I thought she was going to beat the life out of them, but no. She hoisted her sister's knickers like a flag

116

of convenience and stuck the stick in the snow for the biting frost to have a go. I was getting worried about Pempela. If she hung around Aunt Stefa much longer, we would be back where we had started. But I needn't have fretted. Pempela is a clever girl. Discreetly she disappeared, before she could be sent off with a flea in her ear.

17th February 1940

THE frost has eased at last. Days are longer and people are feeling more cheerful on the whole. Yesterday we had another visitation from the Gerries. This time it was a friendly call. Well, as friendly as one could expect from one's enemies. Lieutenant Kirshtein wanted to hold a reunion dinner party for himself and his wife, who was arriving from Germany for a short stay. He said that he's willing to pay all the expenses. What he did not say was that he would provide the food. He took it for granted that the meat and vegetables and everything else that the occasion demands should be our responsibility. The entire job fell into Mama's lap. Today she set about half-heartedly preparing a meal for the Lieutenant and his wife. She managed to get a rabbit by a sheer stroke of luck from the ex-gamekeeper. He does poaching here and there and anywhere he can. Before the war, poachers were sinners, now they are providers, an essential part of the community. They even enjoy more prestige than parsons, though Mama tries to be on good terms with both professions. Mama's task proved to be even more difficult because Lieutenant Kirshtein, although a German, was also a decent fellow. It was hard to dislike him. And if that wasn't enough, he was also a handsome man. Nice inside and outside, as one might say. This fact played havoc with Mama's loyalties. Not enthusiastically at first, Mama put on a clean cloth, then the best china was brought out and even a few crocuses were set in the centre of the table. When every-

117

thing was just about ready, they arrived. Mrs Kirshtein exactly matches her husband. Small, pretty and unassuming, like the nicest person from our own kind. She was grateful for everything. She liked the meal, our house, our family, and it was difficult to regard such agreeable people as something other than friends. So we welcomed them, hoping that perhaps there are more Germans about like the Kirshteins. They said that Mama's dinner was wonderful, and Wojtek's painting of Miss Kolupa absolutely astonishing. Immediately Lieutenant Kirshtein wanted to buy it. Papa pointed out that it had no frame. That didn't matter, they said. They offered fifty zloty for it and Wojtek didn't know what to do. To him it was a fortune, and no doubt he would have parted with it for five zloty. But Papa, who has had a lot of practice in diplomacy, said that the portrait was being prepared for the Art Gallery in Warsaw. It impressed them no end, and they offered another twenty-five zloty, which was a generous gesture. Even Papa had to admit it. So the picture was wrapped, the money was paid and, as they were departing, Aunt Aniela said goodbye in English by mistake. It turned out that the Kirshteins spoke fluent English. So far, Uncle Tadeusz and Papa were struggling to carry on a conversation in German. It mainly consisted of *ja's* and *nein's*. It turned out that Lieutenant Kirshtein is stationed at Zegrze, near the border with the Protectorate, and that he and his wife come from Hamburg. They left their address and were hoping that after the war we might meet again, and then it would be their turn to return the hospitality. Having said *auf wiedersehen*, we all agreed that they were exceptional Gerries. Wojtek was very pleased with the money and gave fifty zloty to Mama and Papa and kept twenty-five himself. He said he would paint another picture of Miss Kolupa, as it is quite plain that she is just the right subject for a portrait. Papa said that it was also Wojtek's talent that sold his picture. Everyone agreed that the "White Witch" was a wonderful piece of work. Wojtek smiled modestly, revealing the faithful half of his tooth. Like Miss Kolupa's tooth, it had the same hypnotic quality.

19th February 1940

PORKY and Cindy are great friends. They sleep together, walk together, and they've even been sharing each other's food, which to Grandpa is a most unnatural thing to do. I don't know whether they have a sort of common language or if it is just a mutual affection that has developed through their circumstances. Anyway, whatever the reason, Porky and Cindy are pals for life. Samson, however, is a different kettle of fish. He remains aloof and regards both Porky and Cindy as unwelcome lodgers. Aunt Stefa tried to introduce little Porky to Samson, but he turned his nose up and refused to have anything to do with a lesser creature than himself. Auntie says that it's Samson's age. He's getting on and he's set in his ways, just like our Grandpa, she added.

22nd February 1940

AUNT Aniela has been sick this morning. Irka said it's the baby that's giving her the trouble. She said that when she was expecting Danúska, she was sick ever so many times. Aunt Aniela doesn't look at all well. Every morning her face turns green. Mama says it's going to be a boy because they are always more troublesome, even before they are born. It is a pity that Aunt Aniela feels sick because we are having doughnuts and *favorki*. I like them both. *Favorki* are made from ordinary flan pastry. Mama rolls out the pastry into a fairly thin sheet and cuts lots and lots of rectangles, ten centimetres by five. Then a slit is made in the middle and one end is threaded through it. This makes them look twisted. Mama fries them in hot oil for just one or two minutes. When they turn a golden colour they are taken out and put on a flat glass dish. I usually sprinkle them with vanilla icing sugar and they are ready to eat. But Mama forbids us to nibble them before the feast and puts them up on the highest shelf so as not to lead us into temptation while the doughnuts were being

119

made. Today our kitchen has been smelling like a posh tearoom. The boys hovered over the frying pan like wasps. As soon as Mama shooed off one, the other two appeared. Jurek actually managed to pinch one doughnut from right under Mama's nose. He said, "Look Auntie, your doughnuts are burning!" And while her attention was on the frying pan he pinched one from the plate and hid it behind his back. Then he ran off before I had the chance to tell Mama what had happened. Jurek is so fast on his feet that no-one can catch him, and that's why he usually gets off scot-free.

25th February 1940

AUNT Aniela is ill in bed. She had a miscarriage. Everybody has been feeling very sorry for her and Uncle Tadeusz is quite upset too. Doctor Kowalski came and said that Aunt Aniela will have to stay in bed for several days, but he did not say why it happened. It was just one of those things, according to Dr Kowalski. Mama made a special dish for her and in the afternoon I went to sit by her bedside. We read *Little Women* together, and she helped me to translate it. It's a lovely story. I like Joe best.

1st March 1940

THE snow has started to melt and there's mud everywhere. Gusts of wind have been shaking the naked trees and tearing off the thatch from the barn next door. It's nasty and cold today and I wouldn't mind staying in bed for the rest of the day, but I can't think of a convincing reason for doing so. Of course, I could say that I've been suffering from lack of intellectual stimulus. Though I doubt if Mama would like that. Ever since Aunt Stefa de-flea'd Pempela, she's been obsessed with the notion that she's caught them herself. Mama says it's nerves. She inspected Auntie's clothes but she found nothing. As a precaution Aunt Stefa has been soaking herself in water scented with lavender. Apparently fleas can't stand that smell, neither can Grandpa. He's been complaining that the whole house pongs like a chemist's shop. It polluted Grandpa's fresh air. Auntie said that she didn't need fresh air and therefore she couldn't see why Grandpa had such a powerful need for it when no-one else had. Grandpa said that the whole place was being turned into a madhouse, and he wasn't going to suffocate. So he banged the door and went off to the stables to purify his lungs.

3rd March 1940

PAPA went away for a day but has been away two days. Mama was very worried, so was I. We wondered what could have happened to Papa. Mama was sure that he'd been arrested. As a result she got a nasty headache. When Mama gets a headache it's really horrible. She has to go to bed and lie down because her temples are splitting and she feels sick. She can't stand any noise or any light and nothing seems to have any effect in easing Mama's pain. The doctor said it's a migraine that Mama is suffering from, and the best thing for her malady is peace and quiet. I drew the curtains while Aunt Stefa tucked Mama into bed with three heated bricks wrapped in towels. When Mama was comfy, I went around telling people to be quiet. Getting Jurek to shut up is as likely as getting a devil to say his prayers. When the house was moderately peaceful and I was hoping that Mama was having a little snooze, Papa arrived. Apparently, nothing had happened to him, that is, nothing unpleasant. He's been visiting his friends and decided to stay the night with them. He said he had a marvellous time, lots of vodka and gossip. I told Papa off which I don't do very often. I said to him that while he was having a good time, poor Mama's been sick with worry, and I hoped he was ashamed for what he did to Mama. I think Papa took to heart my rebuke for he said he was very sorry. The best medicine for Mama's headache was Papa's return. When she woke up and heard he was back, the headache went and Mama was able to get up straight away. This was exactly what Irka was trying to tell me. Husbands do give their wives an awful lot of worry.

6th March 1940

TODAY I gave Pempela a jolly good scrub as her coat was looking pretty grubby after the paraffin treatment. After the bath, which she did not enjoy, I rubbed her dry with a towel and asked her to sit by the stove until her fur was dry. Pempela is usually obedient but sometimes she gets her tantrums. She just would not sit still for more than a couple of minutes. So I gave her a smack across her bottom and told her that she behaved like a common mongrel. This remark of mine upset her. She lay on her tummy with her head in her paws, whimpering. It upset me to see her hurt, so I went and apologised to her. But she wouldn't forgive me at once. She continued to sulk until I gave her a little piece of bread and dripping. When her coat was dry I brushed it. Now she was snowy white and fluffy and her yellow spots had a touch of gilt about them. She was as pretty as a picture. Then I put a few drops of lavender water behind her ears in order to keep those beastly fleas at bay. I told her she could go and see her dog-friend if she liked. But instead she yawned and dropped off like an old lady.

9th March 1940

GRANDPA took Irka, Mama and Aunt Stefa to church, to confession and Holy Communion. Papa didn't go with them because he said God was not interested in his sins. Papa's sins must be very dull. Anyway, he feels that it is far better to concentrate upon positive inclinations rather than dwell upon negative deeds. Grandpa doesn't agree with Papa, and he said so. But Papa wanted to know whether Grandpa had considered poor God, who must be getting pretty fed up at this time of year, having his ears drenched with endless torrents of human folly. Grandpa answered that it was God's job to listen, and anyway He probably enjoyed it. He said that confession does to his soul what senna-pods do to his stomach. Grandpa always feels better after confession. They set off for church before breakfast in Grandpa's best carriage, with a little sunshine from a patchy sky and a modicum of grumbling from Samson, who wasn't feeling too saintly at that time of the morning. Aunt Aniela and I were left in charge of the kitchen. We decided on a simple lunch. Having rejected ten dishes as being too complicated, Aunt Aniela favoured some rice and boiled eggs. For sweet, we felt prunes and chiffon custard would be a nice conclusion. Aunt Aniela put a half-kilo of rice in the saucepan, covered it with cold water and put it on the hot kitchen range. After a slow start, the water began to boil and the rice absorbed every drop. So we added more water and the rice rose right to the top, swelling like mad. Obviously the saucepan wasn't big enough. We transferred the rice into a larger saucepan and boiled it for half-an-hour. Aunt Aniela tasted the mash and decided it was done. Then we hard-boiled seven eggs which took longer than we expected. We should have got the eggs ready first, Aunt Aniela said to me, and I agreed. I asked her whether it might not be a good idea to start cooking the dry prunes and she too agreed with me. In fact we were both pretty agreeable, which makes nonsense of the proverb that too many cooks spoil the broth. As we discovered to our annoyance, dry

123

prunes take a heck of a time to cook. Perhaps we should have soaked them beforehand, but who was to know that? Prunes might be good for the bowels but they are bad for one's temper. Every few minutes we, taking turns, prodded them with a fork and they continued to look and feel as if they had come from Tutankhamen's tomb. Then we remembered the custard. The boys kept on poking their heads around the door, asking whether lunch was ready. It did not help matters, and when Jurek appeared he got what he deserved. Cooking custard was easy when I watched Irka making it. The chiffon "a la me" did not resemble Irka's custard at all. It had a peculiar texture which some unkind person would call lumpy, but Aunt Aniela said it was a different thing altogether. Furthermore, she added, life wouldn't be awfully exciting if everything was always the same. One thing was certain, no-one has ever had a meal like that before. As tea-time approached, the lunch was ready. We piled the mountain of rice onto our biggest dish. Then we arranged the halved eggs around it and stuck a sprig of parsley in the middle to make it look pretty. Just then, it occurred to me that when Irka does that sort of thing she probably washes the parsley first. Anyway, it was too late. The best thing was to scoop out the dirty rice. I did just that, and it looked all right. We put the miserable prunes in a silver bowl and drowned them in custard. I was working on Mama's saying, "What the eye doesn't see, the mouth enjoys." That saying works for Mama but, as I later discovered, it did not work for me. When the famished family sat around the table there was an unusual silence. The lull before the storm. All eyes were focused on the Everest of rice. Aunt Aniela started to dish out. "Not too much for me," said Papa, who is generally well-mannered. "What the hell is that supposed to be?" asked Uncle Tadeusz, who is generally down to earth. Thank goodness the others were out. A little salt and pepper improved Aunt Aniela's dish and I, for one, set a good example by eating every grain of rice, which wasn't difficult because they were sticking together. Unfortunately for me, the prunes and chiffon were not as popular as the main course.

124

That was probably because people's appetites had been ruined by the first course. Still, Wojtek, Tadek and Jurek, having good teeth, managed to chew their way through the prunes and they didn't even notice the lumps in the custard. I must remember it for the future. If you have two bad things, put them together and it helps to disguise their mutual shortcomings. As custom demanded, they all said "thank you" as they got up from the table. We took the remains back into the kitchen, hoping that Mama would know what to do with it. I heard Uncle Tadeusz saying to Papa that God had taken His revenge on them for not going to confession.

11th March 1940

PAPA'S wireless has packed up again. We haven't a clue what is happening on the Western Front. The farmers have started to plough their fields and there's a hint of spring in the air. Everybody feels that things will get better before long. Irka hasn't been feeling too good lately. She gets nasty coughs and her chest is wheezing. Danúska has been teething and she's been crying at night, which makes Irka irritable. Mama said she won't be getting a proper feast for Easter, which is less than two weeks away, because meat is scarce and garlic sausage is very expensive, if one can get it. The chickens and ducks have started to lay and we have plenty of eggs. Mama thinks that there should be enough eggs for *pisanki*. We love making decorated Easter eggs. Needless to say, Wojtek's *pisanki* are always the best. He usually produces some beautiful and unusual designs. People are reluctant to break the shells and many display them on their dressing-tables. Wojtek uses ordinary water paints but he adds a little glue. This makes the pattern look shiny. Mama likes best his Chinese and Japanese designs, with dragons and apple blossom and little pagodas. Last year we had a huge Easter spread. The whole table was covered

with baked meats and cakes, boiled eggs and roast ham. There were
pâtés and stuffed ducks, many different kinds of garlic sausages
and seasonal Easter *mazurki*. Mama's *mazurki* are lovely to look at
and even better to eat. She generally makes the oblong cases from
very rich, sweet pastry, and she varies the fillings according to her
whim. The two I prefer are cheese and sultanas, and fudge and
walnuts. I also like caramel *mazurki*. Papa loves the traditional rum
baba which is made mainly from yolks, sugar and whipped whites
and baked in a clay pot. When it is cold, Mama makes small holes
and pours in some rum which seeps into the cake. Then she makes
some special translucent icing which she pours over the baba.
When Papa samples Mama's Easter baba he always kisses her on
her hand to say thank you. Mama generally says that it isn't as
good as last year's but everybody disagrees with her. However,
before the Easter feast is allowed to begin, Father Jakob comes in
to the dining room dressed in a black cassock and white vestments. He carries a vessel with holy water in one hand and a
sprinkler in the other. The family and the guests stand around the
table wearing their Easter best, and he blesses the food. Papa
always makes sure that his decanter of vodka also gets the
blessing. Then Mama carries a plateful of quartered hard-boiled
eggs and offers them to the guests, wishing them a Happy Easter.
After that the feast begins. People drink and eat and are merry.
When they have had a drop of Papa's "blessed vodka" they really
think that the earth is in Heaven. To me, Easter is a wonderful
holiday. It's not only the joy of the anniversary of Christ's
resurrection, but also the season to greet the spring. Everything in
the garden is waking up from its long winter sleep. The trees and
shrubs are bursting into life with crowns of lime glory. Silver
catkins swing on the willow tresses, and the emerald carpets of
grass are almost too new and too delicate to walk on. There are
usually jonquils and daffodils turning their trumpets towards the
sun, as if playing a fanfare to hail the spring. The crocuses are like
gold chalices holding sweet nectar for the bumble-bees. Everything is beautiful, young and fresh. But the crazy day for our

family begins at the crack of dawn on Easter Monday. People just go mad. Everyone, usually considered sane, goes raving bonkers. We know it's crazy, but we all do it. According to some strange custom, people's clothes and their homes are usually dripping with water. Yes, we simply throw water at each other. On Easter Monday morning, Polish people don't say good morning to each other, they just pour water over their friends. As their enthusiasm grows and their clothes get saturated, cups and pans are replaced by buckets. The floors are drenched with water, the carpets are sodden and the furniture is swamped. People are laughing and screaming, and generally behaving like a pack of lunatics. Usually the feeble females are the worst off. At the end of such a spree they look and feel like wet blankets. After the hysterical laughter, the reproaches, rebukes and undignified rows begin. All this and much more lasts till noon, and everybody thinks that they have had a whale of a time. This is the Polish *Lany Poniedzalek*.

13th March 1940

TADEK, Wojtek and Jurek went to confession yesterday, and today Jurek's behaviour was noticeably better. Though I doubt if he can hold on being good till Easter. I think he should stay in his room, away from all temptations. I noticed last year when he was in his room with a book, he didn't get up to mischief. The trouble with Jurek is that he can't stand his own company, and I am not surprised. Aunt Aniela took us to the woods for a nature walk. We had to observe and record plants, insects, birds and small animals. I had on my list twenty different kinds of plants, seven insects, nine birds and four animals. Jurek, instead of making notes, was pointing out to Aunt Aniela what the birds were doing. Aunt Aniela pretended she couldn't see them. No doubt she wants to stay pure at heart for Easter, which Jurek evidently finds impossible to do. I used to adore walking in the woods on a carpet of pine needles or on the spongy moss, and listen to the forest's noises. Now I always think of the dead soldier. His body is buried somewhere underneath that mossy carpet. The trees are no longer crooning, but they seem to be whispering secrets of what they saw. But we never talk about it in the house, so I didn't like to tell Aunt Aniela that I'd much rather be in the fields, where the wind is blowing and where the newly ploughed soil is looking like a huge milk chocolate bar. It is difficult to believe that only a few weeks ago the whole countryside was covered in snow. And now the trees are turning green and the birds are busy building their nests. I am so glad that spring is here.

19th March 1940

WE'VE been helping Uncle Tadeusz in the garden, not because we volunteered but because Uncle said that we ought to help at this time of year. He's been planting shallots and broad beans. Some of the shallots have already been pulled out by nosy pigeons. Uncle hates pigeons, which are a menace on his smallholding. If he were a better shot, he said, he would provide Mama with a couple for a pigeon pie. Rabbits are non-existent this year. People have already eaten them. If this shortage of meat continues, no doubt people will start eating sparrows. What a horrible thought.

Grandpa is the best ploughman in our family and Samson doesn't mind pulling the plough. Grandpa's furrows are very straight and he takes real pride in neat ploughing. But he also likes to hear people appreciating his skill. Today, Uncle Tadeusz forgot to comment on how nice and tidy the field looks. So Grandpa praised Samson instead. He told him it was the best bit of ploughing he has done and no mechanical cultivator could achieve such indisputable perfection. Samson, in agreement with Grandpa, blew his own trumpet so that everyone around, including Porky and Cindy, could hear it.

22nd March 1940

TODAY is Good Friday and everybody is fasting except Danúska, Pempela, Samson, Cindy and Porky. Grandpa, Mama and Aunt Stefa had nothing to eat all day. Irka, Aunt Aniela and I had only dry bread and some tea. The boys, Uncle Tadeusz and Papa had pickled herrings and boiled potatoes. Uncle said that he needs the food inside him because he does a lot of work. Papa said that he also needs food to help him to think and the boys are always hungry anyway. Grandpa took Mama and Aunt Stefa to church and they also visited Grandma's grave. Irka and Aunt Aniela were busy scrubbing the floors for Easter and I was cleaning the windows. When I finished this unpleasant task, Papa said that they looked even worse than before. Well, perhaps he was right but he needn't have put it like that, especially on a Good Friday when one is trying to be good. When Grandpa returned, he lit a red candle under the cross of Jesus and we spent the whole afternoon quietly with our thoughts.

23rd March 1940

ALTHOUGH we are spending Easter very modestly this year, Mama has been busy today making and baking a chicken and rabbit pie. She put in a lot of vegetables such as carrots and onions to make up for the lack of meat. She had also made a cheese cake and lots of *pierogi* with sauerkraut and dry mushrooms. Mama is boiling them today and we shall have them fried when they are needed. That's how Papa and Uncle Tadeusz like them. Apart from *pisanki* there will be no chocolate Easter eggs this year. Though I made a little chick for Danúska. I made two pom-poms from yellow wool, one big and one small. I joined them together. Then I wound some orange wool around two matchsticks and they were the legs. I fixed two glass beads for eyes and stuck on an orange paper beak which looks quite realistic. I hope Danúska will like her little Easter chick. As a surprise for everybody tomorrow, I shall produce an Easter centrepiece for the table. I have sown some grass seeds on a saucer and already they are lovely and green. I've put a little mirror in, which is supposed to be a lake, and by it I shall put a little china lamb. That'll make the holiday seem more like Easter, I hope.

26th March 1940

I CAN'T remember such a quiet Easter holiday before, but also I can't remember such a lovely sunny day. Returning from church, it was almost like the middle of summer. The warm sunshine was making up for the lack of food and the loss of freedom. The sun shone from early morning till late evening, even when the moon was halfway up the sky. It threaded its golden rays through the beeches and pines making their bark glow like orange torches. Grandpa said we ought to be grateful for a peaceful Eastertide.

1st April 1940

APRIL Fool's Day today! It's a day of fun for us. First thing this morning I went to Tadek and told him that Janka was in the bakery and wanted to see him. Irka and I watched Tadek striding towards the bakery as fast as he could and we were

130

laughing our heads off. Later on I asked Grandpa whether he knew what had happened to Samson, because he wasn't in the stables. Grandpa got very agitated and dashed off to look for him. When Grandpa returned and said that I needed some glasses, I said to him *"Prima Aprilis"* and we both chuckled. Aunt Aniela, in anticipation of what Jurek might get up to, told him yesterday that April Fool's Day has been postponed by the Germans and will be celebrated on May the first. Jurek was quite put out but swallowed it, hook, line and sinker. I think that was very funny. But Aunt Stefa and Mama's joke was best of all. Mama and Aunt Stefa, being identical twins, exchanged their roles. Aunt Stefa put Mama's clothes on and she combed her hair into a bun at the back. She put on Mama's shoes, even her wristwatch and rings, and went into the kitchen and busied herself preparing lunch. She was there for about an hour before Irka and Aunt Aniela recognised her. After that Aunt Stefa, dressed as Mama, went to see Papa and asked him for some money. He gave her a ten zloty note, reminding her that money doesn't grow on trees, and it was only when she was walking off with the cash that he recognised her. Everyone was absolutely rolling about with laughter. We had such a lot of leg-pulling that I shall remember today for many, many years.

2nd April 1940

AFTER the warm spell over Easter, most of the trees and shrubs have been bursting into leaf early, but it is quite plain that our cherry orchard took a hard knock during the severe winter. All the black cherry trees are dead and only a few of the white varieties might be all right. Uncle is very upset and it means a loss of revenue to us all. Uncle Tadeusz and Papa have been marking the trees that have died, and there are a great many. They will be suitable only for logs, which is an awful shame. It also means no more cherry dumplings.

5th April 1940

WE thought the cherry trees being killed by frost was a disaster, but now we have another worry. We've been distressed for the past couple of days. A notification from the Gerries arrived requiring all young men between the ages of sixteen and twenty-five to report to the German police station. They've been told that within two weeks they'll be deported to Germany or East Prussia to work on German farms. This means that our Tadek will have to go. Aunt Stefa is in tears. Tadek took the bad news very bravely indeed. He comforted his mother saying that he'll be all right and she is not to worry on his account. What is happening in Germany, said Papa, is that practically every male in their country has been enrolled into their army, and there isn't anyone left to work in the fields. That's why they are taking our youth. Uncle Tadeusz is fuming with fury. Now it is plain for everyone to see how vulnerable we all are. We have to slave and bow to our dictators.

7th April 1940

MAMA and Aunt Stefa started to get Tadek's things together. We are all busy knitting and mending and patching his clothes. Aunt Aniela has been particularly industrious. She sat till the small hours in the morning finishing a pair of socks and gloves for Tadek. I made him two hankies from an old sheet, and Mama's been sewing a shirt and a pair of pyjamas for him. Now Mama feels that the same thing may happen to Wojtek because he's nearly fifteen.

8th April 1940

UNCLE Tadeusz has been saying to Papa that Borowa-Góra is not as good a place as he thought. Warsaw may well be safer. For example, the Gerries wouldn't consider the people from the city to be a suitable labour force on their farms. They prefer the country yokels like us, who are used to working on the soil, said Uncle. Papa said we couldn't all disappear at once because it would be too conspicuous. Uncle agreed that he and Aunt Aniela might go first. What he really would like to do is to go to Warsaw alone first, and explore the food situation there. Aunt Aniela was very pleased when she heard that Uncle has been considering going back to Warsaw. I have been thinking about Tadek and Janka. Tadek will be very sorry to leave his sweetheart behind. I wonder whether he's told her yet. I haven't seen them together the last few days. So I decided to walk to the shop and break the sad news to her. However, when I got half-way, I saw her coming towards our house. I asked her whether she had heard the news about Tadek. At first she was a little stand-offish with me, but when she heard what I had to say she was rather upset. I told her that Tadek will be back before winter and that he thinks a lot of her. When we got to our house, Janka went into the bakery but I didn't follow her. I felt that she'd much rather be left alone with Tadek. I think Janka loves our Tadek quite a lot and I am truly sorry for both of them. Why do they have to make so many people unhappy? Why do the nasty Gerries have to interfere so much in everyone's life?

11th April 1940

EVERYONE is down in the dumps except Pempela. She's been gallivanting with her new dog-friend. I'm glad the yapping fox-terrier is in the dog-house as far as Pempela is concerned. Apart from his excruciating yapping, and his fleas, he's a poor match for Pempela, that is, from the intellectual angle. Dogs are not unlike people. Those who bark the most think the least. And the fox-terrier is definitely a barker. Papa once said that he's a neurotic dog and he caught the ailment from his owner, Mrs Cybulka. Papa could be right because she is rather a strange person. She's been fraternising with the Gerries. She works at the customs post at Zegrze doing some cleaning and cooking for them. People can't even tell her how much they deplore her behaviour for fear that she'd tell the Gerries. Being at work all day, she leaves her dog roaming around the village, and that's not very nice, not even for that yapper. I'm glad our Pempela has a more respectable and steady friend.

12th April 1940

WE had our first lot of radishes for tea. Uncle Tadeusz has been growing them in a frame and that's why they are ready so early. By now Mama has persuaded people that Cindy's cheese is quite nice really, and anyway there isn't any other cheese available. So, in fact, it boils down to Cindy's cheese or nothing. Nothing is hard to bear for food addicts like us. Mama's made a tasty dish from the cheese and the radishes, which were sliced and mixed with it. It went very well with bread and butter.

Irka says that Pempela is going to have puppies. I wonder whether it was her new sweetheart. Perhaps the lavender behind her ears might have helped. Irka said that Aunt Aniela should try the same. I asked Pempela whether it was true that she's expecting and she was quite coy. Irka must be right. It will be very nice for Pempela to have little puppies, but it won't be nice for Grandpa because he dislikes too many domestic animals about the house. That's why we haven't got a cat. On the other hand he might succumb to the charm of Pempela's puppies, just as he did with Danúska.

18th April 1940

EVER since early morning, Aunt Stefa and Mama have been packing Tadek's trunk. Mama baked an egg and cheese pie for his journey and I made some fudge for him. Everybody is depressed, including Tadek, who is trying not to show it. Janka came at ten o'clock and brought him a bag of boiled sweets. Her eyes were red and she's been blowing her nose quite unashamedly. At about eleven, Grandpa went to harness Samson to the carriage, while Tadek went to say goodbye to our neighbours and friends. They all gave him a little gift to take with him. He returned loaded with parcels and packets as if it were Saint Nicholas' day. Uncle Tadeusz and Papa put Tadek's trunk on the back seat. Auntie Stefa was brushing Tadek's jacket and kept on asking whether he hadn't forgotten this or that. The tears were rolling down her cheeks. Mama was running from Aunt Stefa to Tadek, trying to comfort them both. Wojtek and Jurek were holding Tadek's coat and his briefcase. Tadek's large blue eyes were moist and I could see he was trying so hard to show us that he really was a man. Grandpa put Samson's nose-bag with his feed under the front seat. Uncle Tadeusz said it was time to go if they were to get to Serock on time. Tadek shook hands and kissed everyone including me. He climbed onto the carriage and took his seat next to Grandpa. "Don't forget to write," said Aunt Stefa, wiping her eyes. Grandpa took hold of the reins, clicked his tongue, and Samson reluctantly moved off towards the gate. It was wide open. The neighbours gathered on one side of it. People waved and shouted goodbyes. Tadek waved back. I felt a lump in my throat. I didn't know that I cared so much. The carriage turned into the lime avenue, away from our sight. Janka, holding a bunch of red tulips walked out through the same gate that had, with such indifference, let her sweetheart go.

20th April 1940

THE house seems empty without our Tadek. It's amazing how much space one person can occupy in the house, in our thoughts or in our hearts.

It's Wojtek's birthday today. Because of the gloomy atmosphere in our household, people forgot to wish Wojtek many happy returns. That is, except Mama, Papa and myself. He's fifteen today. Papa gave him some oil paints, and Mama a new pallet and a brush. I gave him two pencils. Pempela licked his hand when I told her that it was his birthday. It is a pity that no-one seems to know when Pempela's birthday is. Irka can't even remember how old our Pempela is. She thinks it could be six or seven years since she was born. She came from the next village as a very small puppy. The owner wanted to destroy her, but Auntie Stefa wouldn't let him and she took her in. She christened her Pempela, which is rather a funny name. But it suited her because our Pempela is a funny bitch. At that time, of course, nobody could have guessed that she would grow up into such a brainy personality. Because of Pempela's condition, I've been giving her some milk, which she drinks all right, but she's not mad about it. However, being a sensible mother-to-be, she knows it's good for her babies, which are getting bigger every day. Her tummy is almost touching the floor. I don't think anyone knows how many puppies she's going to have, not even Pempela herself.

23rd April 1940

UNCLE Tadeusz has been away for the past two days. He's gone to Warsaw to weigh up the political and economic situation there. Aunt Aniela can hardly wait to get back to her mother and her friends. Grandpa doesn't want Uncle to leave his house because there won't be anyone suitable to see to the garden. Papa hasn't got any natural or any acquired inclinations towards gardening. He said that he wasn't born with green fingers, and everyone believes him. When Papa touches a plant it turns brown. Wojtek is a bit like Papa, though he can tell the difference between the weeds and the plants. I don't particularly like working in the garden but I can do it if I have to. Jurek sometimes works hard, very often not so hard, and frequently not at all. That leaves only Mama, Aunt Stefa and Grandpa, who is rather old and he finds that, as he is nearing the soil, the soil gets further away from him. We all feel terribly unsettled just now and are hoping that something good will soon happen somewhere.

27th April 1940

UNCLE Tadeusz returned from Warsaw last night with some good news about the Western Front. Apparently, seven German destroyers were sunk by the British. Also, some British troops have landed in Norway. Three cheers for our dear allies! I'm sure one day the whole world will salute that noble country. In Warsaw things are not so good but it could have been a great deal worse, said Uncle Tadeusz. Inflation is raging and there is a shortage of food, but one can get many essentials on the black market. Uncle Tadeusz and Aunt Aniela will be leaving us as soon as they can fix their transit through the border. Now it is possible to bribe the Gerries who are patrolling the bridge. All one has to do is to give them what they want and in return, on a certain date and at a certain time, the patrol will just turn their backs on the bridge over the Bug, and one can simply walk across without being stopped or molested in any way. That's what Aunt Aniela and Uncle Tadeusz are planning to do. I don't want them to go. It won't be the same without Aunt Aniela. She's more like a friend to me. I can talk to her like I talk to Irka. And I shall miss my lessons. Aunt Aniela enjoys words better than work, and she manages to look smart even when she's scrubbing the floor. Uncle Tadeusz is fond of her, but not her cooking. Aunt Aniela says that she's allergic to cooking. But even so, Uncle Tadeusz and Aunt Aniela get on quite well together and Papa says it's because they both drive on different tracks and the likelihood of a collision is negligible. I think Mama and Papa are driving on the same track, but in the same direction. Papa once confessed that he couldn't live without Mama's cooking. Whether this applied to Mama as a whole, he didn't say. Mama couldn't live without Papa because she needs his money for a start, and she is also fond of Papa because he's charming. Aunt Stefa said that he could even charm a nightingale if he wanted to. I think Papa has to be charming so that people can easily forgive him for working not too hard.

28th April 1940

DANÚSKA is six months old and she can sit up, and say Mama and Baba. She's so pretty, and Irka thinks her to be the best looking baby in both our villages. Mama's made a little dress for Danúska from my old dress, and she crocheted an edging on the sleeves and around the neck. It looks very nice. Wojtek has made some wooden bricks which he painted in bright colours. She likes to play with them. Now that the weather is warm, I take Danúska in her pram for some fresh air and at the same time I can have a gossip with my friends in the village. Janka asked me if we have had a letter from Tadek yet. I told her it's only ten days since he left home and the post is not functioning as well as it did before the war. I promised Janka to let her have his address as soon as we hear from him. Janka told me that she's missing Tadek very much and she's worried that he'll forget her and probably find some other girls in the new big world. I said Tadek would never do that, because he's very much in love with her. I said that Tadek would have a job to find a better looking girl than herself. And, furthermore, she had the best pair of legs in the village. Even Wojtek had said so. Janka was very pleased to hear that and it cheered her up a great deal. When I was pushing Danúska back, I could not help feeling that our Danúska will grow up to be even better looking than Janka.

30th April 1940

ON the last day of the month we had an April shower. Uncle Tadeusz is very pleased because it is good for the garden. Porky is also pleased because it left a few puddles. Porky is like me, he likes paddling. He has grown tremendously but no-one has so far suggested to have him slaughtered. I am so glad because I couldn't stand that. Even Uncle Tadeusz is fond of Porky, and although he doesn't look as dainty as he used to when he was little, he is our pet and we all love him dearly. Even Samson takes much more notice of him since he's doubled in size. Porky likes Aunt Stefa best because she massages his tummy. He lies on his side and his face assumes an expression of utter ecstasy. He closes his eyes and he chortles away as Auntie makes a fuss of him. Cindy likes Irka best because she milks her. Behind the stables, Grandpa has a small plot of land which is suitable for Cindy and Porky to roam in the fresh air. I don't think they are a problem to anyone and they certainly are an asset to us, expecially Cindy who is very generous with her milk.

1st May 1940

TODAY Danúska nearly choked herself to death, but for our clever Pempela. Danúska was playing with buttons and she put one in her mouth. There wasn't anyone about the kitchen just at that moment except Pempela, who was investigating her bowl. When she noticed Danúska choking, she ran to Mama and started barking as loud as she could and led Mama to Danúska, who was getting blue in the face. Mama put her finger in Danúska's throat and, thank the Lord, managed to get the button out. Everybody's been praising and patting Pempela and telling her what a good and intelligent creature she is. Pempela adores being praised but she also likes people to show their gratitude in an appropriate way. So I got her a large piece of bread with plenty of dripping on it, which Pempela thoroughly enjoyed. Mama told Irka that she mustn't leave any small objects around in the kitchen because Danúska puts everything into her mouth. She told Irka that Wojtek was like that when he was a baby. He wanted to taste everything. Mama said that I was much more sensible when I was little, and far less trouble. "But of course," I said, and we all laughed, relieved that a near tragedy turned out to be only a lesson.

3rd May 1940

UNCLE Tadeusz and Aunt Aniela are planning to leave Borowa-Góra after Whitsun. It will be a shame but I suppose we shall get used to it in time. This morning the very first letter from Tadek arrived and we were all ears. He has been posted to East Prussia, near the historical town of Malbork. He's working on a large farm which consists of many acres of arable land, and with cattle, pigs and poultry. There are only two old German farmers and one woman looking after the farm. Poor Tadek has to get up at six o'clock in the morning. He gets one hour for a lunch break and then he works till eight in the evening. Apart from missing us, and the hard work, Tadek seems to be all right. He gave us a detailed account of his journey in a lorry with other young Poles. Luckily, working at the farm there's another fellow from Radom. At least Tadek has a Polish friend there. Aunt Stefa read and re-read Tadek's letter for the umpteenth time. We are all relieved that he's safe and sound. At once I wrote Tadek's address on a piece of paper and dashed off to the shop. I should have known. Janka had also received a letter from Tadek. I could see by the look of her eyes, which sparkled with inner happiness. I shan't tell Auntie Stefa that Janka's letter was two pages longer than hers. But I am sure she would appreciate that Tadek had different things to say to Janka than to his mother.

Now that Tadek is away, Wojtek and Jurek have to help Uncle Tadeusz on the smallholding. Even Papa's been planting potatoes. Auntie Stefa asked him whether he'd made sure that he planted them the right way up. She said that they won't come up if they are upside down. Papa got really worried. Although, as he has told us, his fingers aren't green, he himself seems to be that very colour. That is, as far as gardening goes. Papa dashed off to the field, dug out one potato, and only then did it dawn on him that perhaps his sister-in-law was pulling his leg. Poor Papa, I don't think he'll ever truly understand nature's ways. To him they are a mystery, just like cooking is to Aunt Aniela.

4th May 1940

THERE is something seriously wrong with Danúska's eye. I have been playing with her. It's a little game that she particularly enjoys. I covered one of her eyes with my hand and noticed that she couldn't see at all. So, very gently, I pressed my finger over her eyelid and that eyeball was not as firm as the other eyeball. I've told Irka about it. We've tested her eyesight by covering first the right eye, then the left eye, while offering her a biscuit. She just couldn't see that biscuit with her left eye. Irka went to talk to Mama and we again inspected Danúska's eye. Mama said that Irka should seek some medical advice straight away. In the afternoon, Grandpa drove Irka, Mama and Danúska to Dr Kowalski's surgery. When they returned, our fearful suspicions were confirmed. Little Danúska was blind in one eye due to a disease which Dr Kowalski could not diagnose without special tests. He gave Irka a letter which she is to take to the hospital at Nowy Dwór. Irka was stunned by this revelation, too shocked to cry, but her face betrayed anguish and fear. We tried to console her as well as we could. Though Danúska was as cheerful as if nothing was wrong. She played with the bricks Wojtek made for her and talked to herself. I still can't believe such an awful tragedy should have struck such a little innocent child.

6th May 1940

ACCORDING to the specialist at the hospital, Danúska's eye has been affected by a strain of bacillus and her left eye has been permanently damaged. The specialist said that Danúska will have to undergo an immediate operation if the sight in her other eye is to be saved. While investigating the likely source of infection, they examined Irka and found that she is suffering from tuberculosis herself. It was like a blow with a hammer. Mama was also shocked and she was glad that she went with Irka to the hospital. This dreadful news was too much for anyone to bear. Mama and I went upstairs and had a good cry. Everybody was heartbroken about Irka's tragedy. Grandpa took little Danúska in his arms and sat in his favourite chair, praying to God for help. Having only one eye himself, he knows exactly what it is like to lose one's sight. While Grandpa's lips moved in a silent prayer, Danúska played with his rosary, quite oblivious of the misery we all felt.

7th May 1940

IRKA and Danúska went to Nowy Dwór early this morning. They'll stay there for two weeks at least. Meanwhile, we are hoping and praying that the doctors will be able to cure them both.

Gardening was the theme today. We've been weeding the turnip patch. Uncle Tadeusz thought it was safer to keep Papa at bay. He pulls everything out including Uncle's precious seedlings. Uncle Tadeusz feels it's too late to teach Papa the difference between, say, a turnip and a stinging nettle. As far as Papa is concerned, they are both green and they both sting. Not many people have been stung by a turnip, but Papa has. So Papa's muscles were put to the test in the stables, shifting by-products. Papa is not partial to the scent of manure either. It has the same effect on Papa as lavender has on Grandpa. To be blunt, Papa thinks it stinks to high Heaven. Actually, I agree with him. When he had finished that job, Mama had to disinfect him with carbolic, because somehow he had managed to get the stuff all over himself. Even after a meticulous scrub, one could still tell that Papa had been in the room by the smell he left lingering behind. So they've banished poor Papa from the dining room until he had been out in the fresh air. Papa said that while he was suffering in that stable, his so-called friends were continuously adding towards his misery. Papa feels that this obnoxious pong got under his skin, and he is sure that he needs something more drastic, such as a transfusion of new blood. Nobody said it aloud, but everybody came to the conclusion that it was far less trouble to leave Papa to his thoughts, rather than force him to work on the soil. It was like teaching a turtle to do the tango.

8th May 1940

THE British have had to pull out from Norway, and the Germans are advancing towards Holland. We are very sad to hear that, in particular after the good news a little while back.

Wojtek has been growing so fast that everything seems to be too small for him. I think he's turning into a man too. Jurek is still as he was, full of beans at the wrong times. I am sure he would make a good clown. He's been performing conjuring tricks. He swallowed a lighted cigarette, two combs, and now Mama's been complaining that we are short of forks.

Aunt Stefa had a visit from her ex-boyfriend who has emerged from hibernation now that the month of May has warmed up his corpuscles. Aunt Stefa invited him to the small salon, which during the winter is used for the storage of cabbage-heads. She asked him to sit down while she went to put some lavender behind her ears. I hope Mr Leon hasn't an aversion to lavender like our Grandpa. Evidently not, because he stayed to tea, which Mama brought in on a special tray. She had no fresh biscuits, so she provided the best china instead. While Mr Leon was quenching his thirst behind that closed door, Jurek was doing his best to get in there. He did not succeed, for Mama made quite sure that her twin sister was left completely on her own with Mr Leon.

9th May 1940

WE have been doing the spring cleaning today, which is pretty late. But we all agreed that it is better late than never, and got down to harnessing all spare hands. It's amazing how the gentlemen seem to disappear when they are needed in the house to shift the furniture or to help with other heavy tasks. Grandpa dislikes spring cleaning even more than washing. After lunch he likes to sit in his chair and have a quiet snooze. But with so much rumpus all around the house, Grandpa did Jurek's vanishing act, just like Papa and Uncle Tadeusz had already done. We've been beating the dust out of the curtains, and by the look of them, beating the life out of our tattered rugs. They might have holes in them, but they're clean, said Aunt Aniela. Cleaning the brass is another job that gives instant results, though not without an awful lot of elbow-grease. After I'd cleaned the eighth curtain rail and all the brass rings, I was quite sure I wouldn't have them in my house. When the floors were scrubbed and the cobwebs swept away, the house looked lighter and more cheerful. My next task was to keep on reminding the boys to wipe their feet. But people took no notice. So Aunt Aniela hit upon the idea of charging five groszy as a penalty for everyone who crossed the threshold without wiping their feet. That was a good way of getting some pocket money I discovered.

11th May 1940

TOMORROW is Whitsun and we've been busy decorating the house with green branches and flowers. I picked masses of bluebells and lilies of the valley, peonies and narcissi, and a large bunch of lilac. Aunt Aniela arranged the flowers and I put the greenery behind the pictures. When we'd finished decorating, the dining room looked and smelt like the garden does in May. The scent of lilac hung in the air, mixed with the delicate perfume of the peonies. Mama was very pleased with our efforts and we were even more pleased with Mama's. For in spite of shortages, somehow she succeeded in making several different kinds of cakes and jellies with sliced pears. She also stuffed hard-boiled eggs with a mixture of cheese, gherkins and pickled herrings. In the evening, we pressed our spring outfits, cleaned our shoes, and everything is set for tomorrow.

12th May 1940

EVERYBODY went to church today, including Papa and Uncle Tadeusz. The gentlemen walked and the ladies rode in the carriage. Samson wasn't in a hurry, neither was Grandpa, so we arrived at the church half-way through the service. The church was packed with people, spilling out into the churchyard. "Ave, ave Maria," their voices lilted into the air. I am sure that God could hear the cry from their hearts. He was here, among us, for those who believed in Him. When we got back, we had a cold salad lunch. The kaleidoscope of greens and lime and lemon with red radishes and beetroots almost bedazzled the eye. The spectacle was grand. Our Whitsun spread would have dignified any royal table. The art of Mama's cuisine lies in the indisputable fact that she alone can do so much with so little.

14th May 1940

THE holiday is over and the best china has been put away. Uncle Tadeusz and Aunt Aniela have also gone away. It seems so quiet without Uncle's robust voice, and so dull without pretty Aunt Aniela. The dining table is now too big for our shrinking clan. Though Pempela has set the numbers right. Last night, or it could have been early this morning, she brought us three adorable puppies. Two black and white, with the looks of her sweetheart, and one just like herself, white and yellow. Only there's more yellow than white — like scrambled eggs. Yes, I'll call him Scrambles if Pempela approves of the name. She looked so proud and so pleased with her babies. They were having their breakfast when I went to the barn to say hello. I took some refreshments for Mama-Pempela and a bowl of fresh water. I swear she was saying thank you with her amber eyes.

16th May 1940

IT'S my birthday today and I have reached the age of eleven. Since my last birthday I have grown five centimetres, which is not bad at all. It's probably because it has been a long year. I had a history book from Mama and Papa, and Wojtek has made me a wooden frame for Danúska's photograph. Jurek gave me his book on magic but it disappeared even before I had the chance to look at it. Janka brought me a brooch, a four-leaf lucky clover. I invited her to tea because Mama and Aunt Stefa gave me a special cherry cake. Mama baked it and Aunt Stefa sprinkled it with sugar.

Next Thursday Grandpa is going to the hospital to fetch Irka and Danúska. They are both feeling much better. I've missed them quite a lot. We had a letter from Uncle Tadeusz and Aunt Aniela. They are glad to be in Warsaw and they have invited me to join them. Aunt Aniela has a place for me at the school where she is teaching. Mama wants me to go to school. She says it's a chance in a hundred and, if she were me, she would jump at it. The

146

truth is that I am not at all sure how I feel about going to Warsaw. One half of me wants to go to school, and the other half wants to stay here, with my loved ones. I expect Mama and Papa will decide for me, as they always do. This is almost my last entry in my secret diary because I have filled nearly all the pages. I thought it was going to last me years and years. But so much has happened in one year that the past twelve months seem to me like two years.

17th May 1940

MAMA and Aunt Stefa have been preparing a bedroom for Irka and Danúska. Now that Aunt Aniela and Uncle Tadeusz are gone, we have plenty of room, and they both deserve some comfort after that terrible ordeal. I helped Mama. With some fresh straw I stuffed the mattress until it was bulging like a balloon. They should be nice and comfy on it. Mama and I carried the big eiderdown outside to air. We spread it on four chairs in a sunny part of the garden. Aunt Stefa changed the sheets and pillow-cases. I spread Danúska's toys on the window sill. Then I picked a bunch of red, blue and yellow pansies, and placed the posy on the bedside table. Grandpa brought in a Bible because he knows that Irka likes reading, and Mama put a chamber-pot under the bed. Aunt Stefa said that the chamber-pot needed scrubbing and she looked at me. I always seem to get landed with potty jobs, and when I asked why, she said that I had the right touch. Right touch, my foot! It's more likely that Aunt Stefa wanted to be relieved of the burden. This particular chamber-pot, she added, is a family heirloom. It has an aristocratic ring about it. Grandma had claimed that it belonged to the Romanoffs. And she was always very particular who used that pot, because, according to Grandma, no less a person than His Royal Highness Czar Nicholas II had sat upon it. Aunt Stefa told me that story to make the job of scrubbing it more interesting. Well, it didn't. To me a pot is a pot and I don't care who's sat on it and who has not!

20th May 1940

TODAY I said goodbye to Mama, Papa, Wojtek and every-one at Grandpa's house. For I am on the train which is taking me to Warsaw. We had a message from Aunt Aniela yesterday that arrangements have been made for me to cross the border today at eleven o'clock. Hastily, Mama packed my small case, saying that my other things will be sent on at a later date. She washed my hair and tied it with new ribbons. I put on my white socks and shoes, my red pleated skirt and jacket, and my white hat. Mama tied a long scarf into a bow under my chin. She kissed me on the cheek and explained that, for my own good, I should now go off to school. I looked at Papa, and hugged him. But he, too, said that school was the right place for me. I went to say my farewells to Pempela and the puppies, to Samson, Cindy and Porky, and to tell them how much they all mean to me. I took a final look at the pear trees in flower, and the apple trees covered in blossom with their delicate petals blushing under the gaze of the morning sun. I walked for the last time along the alley edged with blue lupins and red larkspurs and sniffed the waterfall of cascading roses. Oh, that scent, that lovely purple scent, rising like incense into the dewy air. Mama called me and it was time to go. Samson clip-clopped along the cobbled road and Mama sat holding my hand. I wanted to weep, but why? It was for my own good, as Mama and Papa had said before. And all too soon we were there. I kissed Grandpa and Mama goodbye and was told to hurry. "But what if they catch me?" Nobody was going to catch me, said Mama. All I have to do is to walk across that bridge, just like any other bridge, until I get to the other side. "And then what?" Just show your ticket at the station and get on the train. Aunt Aniela will meet you when you arrive in Warsaw, Mama assured me. I hurried along, clutching my case, which seemed like clutching at a straw. What a long bridge. I looked back at Mama. She was waving and I waved back. I started to run. Deep waves of foaming water twisted and twined beneath my feet. That seething serpent was going to swallow me if I fell in. I'd never get to the other end. I looked back to Mama, but she was gone. I was the only soul on this lonely strip of iron. My hands were damp when I reached the other end. Thank goodness, the familiar station was still standing there, and the train was waiting at the usual platform. The conductor asked, "Warsaw?" and punched my ticket. I went into a third class compartment and sat on a wooden seat with my case at my side. There was an old lady, fast asleep, sitting opposite. Her head was drooping like a wilted flower. The engine blew its whistle and clouds of steam blocked out the view. The train moved off, gathering speed. I have taken out my diary to finish these last pages. There is a smell of stale smoke, and a cigarette-end on the floor. I can hear German voices from the next carriage. It looks and feels as if I am in a foreign country. "Warsaw — Praga!" the conductor bellows in Polish. "There you are, you're still in Poland," I said to myself, as if I were talking to Pempela.

Dear Mama and Papa,

I got across (you know what) quite safely and just managed to catch the train to Warsaw, with three minutes to spare. Aunt Aniela was waiting for me at the ticket barrier. We were pleased to see each other and we kissed and hugged and hugged. At Nowogrodzka I have a whole room to myself (the old salon) and Aunt Aniela has filled the shelves with lots and lots of books. I am going to read them all. I shall miss you and Pempela quite a lot, and Wojtek too. Next week I'll send you a long letter and all the news from Warsaw. Apart from thousands and thousands of (you know who) the city looks more or less the same except that no-one seems to be smiling.

That's all for now. Love to you and everybody at Borowa-Góra.

Your loving,

NIUSIA

P.S. Are Irka and Danúska back from the hospital yet?
P.P.S. How are Pempela and her puppies?

THE END

Epilogue

THE four years I spent in Warsaw during the German occupation are a story in themselves. I lived with my aunt in Nowogrodzka Street. In the mornings I attended an ordinary school and in the afternoons private tuition classes, called *komplety*, held in various people's houses. These classes were initiated to teach children the subjects forbidden by the Germans, such as Polish literature and history. While there, I was introduced to an underground Scout movement. In 1942 I became a Girl Guide. This was a secret organisation attached to the Polish Underground Army. We had meetings once a week at which we were taught first-aid and self-discipline.

On 1st August, 1944, the historic Insurrection began in the city of Warsaw. The Girl Guides were called upon to do their duty. I packed my first-aid kit and went to take up my post in Koszykowa Street. The Uprising lasted sixty-three days, and when it was finally crushed, I was among those taken to Germany as prisoners of war. We were eventually liberated in early May, 1945. Together with other women of all ages I was sent to recuperate in a camp at Murnau in Bavaria. Soon all the young girls were moved to Materata in southern Italy, where a Polish school was established under the auspices of General Anders' army. After a few months the school was transferred to England and reopened near Cirencester. Having matriculated, I went for a holiday to Sutton Veny in Wiltshire, where I met my future husband, Alan. I continued my education at Salisbury and then at Millfield School in Somerset. In 1950 I moved to London where I read chemistry. My career was in the research department of a large company in the suburbs of London. In 1953 Alan and I were married.

The first opportunity to return to my native land occurred in August 1965, just twenty-one years after I had left Poland. There

151

was a wonderful reunion with my parents and relations. The small village of Borowa-Góra showed little sign of change since the war years, though some members of my family were no longer alive. But Aunt Stefa was still living there. When we visited her, I was given a box which contained some of my possessions from the past. Among them I found my secret diary. Amused and moved, I translated it into English.

After a month's holiday in Poland, Alan and I came home, though determined to go back again soon. This we did in 1967. Some of my relatives were now living abroad. One of these was my brother Wojtek, who had settled in Sweden. He and his wife Inga, with their daughter, lived in Örebro. He had become a distinguished painter and sculptor of international repute. Several exhibitions of his work were staged in Stockholm, Paris and New York. Tragically, Wojtek died in 1975.